írísḷ

flames

Peter Waller's true story of the arrival of the Black and Tans

John Waller

YIANNIS BOOKS

Acknowledgements

Without my half-brother Peter Waller, this book would never have been written. I thank him not only for the words but also for the depth of feeling with which he describes the fight for freedom of the Irish people. It is a lesson worth remembering today.

Published in 2006 by **YIANNIS BOOKS**
101 Strawberry Vale, Twickenham, TW1 4SJ UK
Tel. 0044 2088923433, 0044 7811351170

First published in UK March 2006
Reprinted in UK June 2006

Typeset by Mike Cooper, 25 Orchard Rd, Sutton SM1 2QA
Printed by Antony Rowe, Chippenham, Wiltshire

www.yiannisbooks.com
'True stories of history, drama and romance'

208pp
ISBN 0-9547887-2-9

Irish Flames

HISTORICAL BACKGROUND

In 1914, the British Parliament passed, but did not implement, the Irish Home Rule Bill, which devolved power from Westminster to Dublin and Belfast. By then, 24,000 rifles had already had been landed in Ulster. In response, the long-distance yachtsmen Erskine Childers, ex-House of Commons clerk and author of *Riddle of the Sands*, and Anglo-Irishman Conor O'Brien ran guns into the South. Then came the First World War during which 49,000 Irishmen gave their lives to fight for the freedom, from German occupation, of another small country like their own – Belgium.

In 1917, American President Woodrow Wilson declared that 'every nation which, like our own, wishes to live its own life and determine its own institutions should be assured of justice and fair dealing by other peoples of the world as against force and selfish aggression'.

In the General Election of 1918 Sinn Féin, the party which demanded freedom from British rule, won 73 out of the 105 seats in all Ireland.

In 1919, the world's politicians gathered at the Peace Conference in Paris to decide the fate of the myriad of small nations. Erskine Childers was there in the Irish delegation but the British blocked the Irish wish to have their case discussed. President Wilson's vision of self-determination had been pushed aside.

By 1920, the strength of the British Army in Ireland had reached nearly 80,000. To these were added 7,000 irregulars, the Black and Tans, to bolster the Royal Irish Constabulary whose officers were resigning in droves.

'Shoot and shoot with effect'

In June 1920, Colonel Smyth, Divisional Police Commissioner for Munster, addressed the police at Listowel, County Kerry:

'Should the order ("Hands Up") not be immediately obeyed, shoot and shoot with effect. If the persons approaching [a patrol] carry their hands in their pockets, or are in any way suspicious-looking, shoot them down. You may make mistakes occasionally and innocent persons may be shot, but that cannot be helped, and you are bound to get the right parties some time. The more you shoot, the better I will like you, and I assure you no policeman will get into trouble for shooting any man.'

He then asked the first constable, 'Are you prepared to co-operate?'

The man curtly referred him to the spokesman whom the members of the Listowel force had chosen, who replied:

'By your accent I take it you are an Englishman and in your ignorance forget that you are addressing Irishmen.' The constable then took off his cap, belt and sword (bayonet) and laid them on the table saying:

'These, too, are English. Take them as a present from me and to hell with you – you are a murderer.'

From *THE IRISH REPUBLIC* by Dorothy MacArdle

To Peter

Now rest in peace

Your story has been published

Thank you for so many happy times

Author's Note

My father was an Irishman; so why am I English?

On Saturday June 14 1930, he stayed with his friend, Conor O'Brien, in Foynes, Co. Limerick. Next morning he set sail, along the circumnavigation route taken seven years before by Conor in his yacht *Saoirse* (Freedom), in his own epic single-handed cruise to the Canary Islands in his 26ft yawl. Returning home on the Yeoward Line s/s Aguila, he fell in love – with my mother.

Back in Ireland he had a problem: he was already married with a son, Peter.

Recently I decided it was time to re-discover my roots. I went back with a sense of guilt. In the 1920s he won a medal in the Tailteann Games, the 'Irish Reconciliation Olympics', had been almost unbeatable as a yachtsman on Lough Derg and had been a scratch golfer at Birr and Portmarnock – he was a real Irish sportsman. But his English wife had been so different – she loved her books and her garden.

I then found a family 'secret'. I no longer felt guilty. Details were impossible to come by until I searched through the shopping bags of family papers, letters and photos my brother Peter had given to me before his death in 1990. I found he had written his childhood story. It told of the War of Independence, the arrival of the Black and Tans and details of the 'secret'.

During my research, I have traced the people and places in the story. In respect for the past and the sensitivity of the present, I have changed their names.

JOHN WALLER
November 2005

The way is blocked

Alec Casemond, built like a bull, short and square, now in his mid-thirties and matured from four years in the War, drove carefully. He had already crossed, with difficulty, a damaged bridge. One side wall, blown away by a mine, revealed below in a swirling river, an almost submerged army lorry. There remained of the bridge barely enough for a donkey cart to pass over. Slowly and in silence he manoeuvred the car across what seemed an interminable distance. His wife Meli had been free to walk, but eight-year-old Robin, lying helplessly on the back seat, with a broken leg, could but trust in him. Alec's relief in successfully negotiating this gruesome reminder of his country's plight gave him new energy and courage.

In that early summer of 1920 the political storm clouds had gathered around Ireland. The dream of Independence, for which the blood of seven centuries had so often flowed, appeared as elusive and remote as ever. Promises, half promises and innuendoes evaporated, leaving first disillusionment, then bitterness and now open and active hostility.

During the spring of 1920 a crowning insult had been inflicted upon a harassed and poverty-stricken Ireland, when English jails provided 'soldiers' considered suitable to deal with the Irish question. These misfits of society were of a low mentality and largely unemployable and dangerous. What an ironic solution it was to give them a free hand in Ireland, thus relieving the pressure on the overburdened British prisons.

Training was unnecessary, since discipline was neither expected nor required. Not even the tradition of a conventional uniform was important. In their thousands they came, a motley crew of murderers, the 'Black and Tans', some wearing black trousers and tan jackets, others khaki trousers and black jackets. They looked, and indeed many proved to be, material for the hangman's noose.

As mile followed mile, Alec thought of former years. At the same age as Robin, his father had drowned in a tragic accident on the Shannon. He had died with his eldest daughter in his arms as he tried to release her from the rigging of the overturned boat. Alec's grandfather, a giant of a man and bare-fist boxing champion of the county, had then told him that, as soon as he was a man, he would take over the family firm.

After prep-school in Dublin, Alec had gone to the United Services College in Westwood Ho!, Devon, where he had learnt to box and where his passion for sport had taken him on to the dunes of the golf links and out to sea in a dinghy. Now he wanted to bring his son up in the same way. It was a result of this drive that had caused Robin to break his leg at the Raheen Regatta.

This year the Regatta had somehow gone wrong all round. Robbie had been taken under the wing of young Martin McCarthy who, though still in his twenties, was headman at Ardmore Castle and was working during the Regatta on the Kernahans' yacht. But then Alec had driven Robin too hard so he had fallen. Meli too had not enjoyed the Regatta. She made little attempt to get on with Alec's friends, and indeed seemed to make more of an effort to talk to Martin who had been so kind to Robbie. Now this journey seemed to be equally jinxed.

They motored on, the winding road meandering its way through sleepy farms and long stretches of bogland. Irish roads of those days were the sad heritage of long decades of indifference and poverty. Yet to come to Ireland were the tarred surfaces of more modern lands. Over this very land, he had on several occasions followed the hounds. Not many miles ahead stood a large military barracks, garrisoned in former times by friendly British troops. There, he and Meli, his young English wife, had danced to the strains of the waltz and the two-step, in the dawn of 1913.

Now the countryside stood still and heavy. Tall hedges sprouting with spring may-blossom frequently concealed desperate patriots bent on ambush. They passed little traffic and even the heavy laden farm carts seemed sad and furtive. Beyond the next sharp corner stood, Alec well remembered, a double row of tall trees. Instinctively, he slowed down; trouble, he knew not what, lay ahead. Only moments were to delay his curiosity, for as the corner ended, he saw again the work of desperate hands. The tall trees no longer stood in dignified formation. Sawn at the base, they lay as a fallen herd of giant animals. He stepped from the car and all around hung an ominous silence. The work was recent and complete. Each trunk showed bright new wood, revealed by a hungry crosscut saw. No longer was the road a thoroughfare but only a graveyard for those mighty trees, which had watched time pass by.

Robin, lying on the seat, knew nothing of their new hazard. 'Dad, I'm hungry. Can we have our picnic now?' Bravo for the mind of a child.

'A grand idea, my boy, and just what the doctor ordered. Meli, come back to earth and dig out that hamper.'

'Yes, oh yes indeed, Alec!' Meli's voice was distant, but she tried to catch her husband's forced enthusiasm.

Here in this remote countryside, once so friendly, she was face to face for the first time with a grim realisation. The tragic sight ahead was the work of men in deadly opposition to her own countrymen. Yet, here was she, married to an Irishman in whose veins ran blood akin to theirs. The quick flashback to an English home, safe and secure in the Edwardian England which she had left, brought little comfort. This forlorn little trio, of which she was one, marooned on a wild and empty road with a row of huge tree trunks blocking ahead, faced a different, hostile world.

Quietly she unpacked the sandwiches, forcing a gentle smile, as she handed the fattest one back to Robin.

'Do you think they will hurt me much at the hospital? Oh! I hope they won't keep me long. Mummy, will you promise to stay in Dublin, even if Dad wants to go back home to Merlin? Will I have to be in bed all the time? Oh! I do want to see Dublin.'

'Now Robbie, I thought you were hungry and you haven't even started that sandwich.' Melissa smiled again.

Alec lit a cigarette. He had no heart to eat. What was he to do? His son lay crippled behind him; his English wife sat at his side. The road back would not get his boy to the hospital treatment he needed, yet directly ahead lay the work of desperate hands.

His thoughts were interrupted by Robin's groan: 'Oh! How my back aches. Please let me sit up for a few minutes so that I can look out and see where we are.' Meli and Alec exchanged a hurried glance. Both knew they wanted the boy to look only out at the back of the car; the forward view was not pleasant.

'O.K., old boy. You lie still for a minute and I will be back.' Alec took an empty bottle which had contained water and walked to a gate at the side of the road behind them. On the gatepost, he placed the bottle and returned with a handful of small stones. 'Now Robbie, I'll help prop you up and we will see who can break the bottle first.' Since his accident, the boy had had no excitement and his cheeks now flushed with glee.

'Come on Mum! See if you can beat us.' Robin held out his handful of stones.

'No darling. You try and beat Daddy, while I pack the picnic.' Meli was aware that they could not stay in this silent half world – its atmosphere strained and ominous.

The bottle was far from Robin, and his cramped position gave him little chance of success. As each stone fell short, Alec matched it with care. Soon he was obliged to fetch a new consignment, for the boy was happy and engrossed. Meli, facing backwards, watched intently and tried to cheer both her husband and her son.

As they paused to count the remaining stones, the sound of breaking glass tinkled through the air. The bottle was there no more. An invisible hand had done their work for them. In front of the car's bonnet stood three men. Each wore a shabby blue coat and a brown slouch hat, and each carried a gun. In silence, they surveyed the occupants of the car.

Meli's hand went quickly to Alec's arm. Her fingers tightened, saying: 'Patience, danger!' For several seconds, no one spoke and nothing moved. Time stopped.

At last, the tallest of the three strange men gave a curious smile: 'There's not a real shot amongst ye, or so t'would seem.'

'Oh, was it you that broke our bottle? You must have played our game often. He's good, isn't he Dad?' piped Robin, as the tall man nodded. Robin had cracked the ice, but a tense aura still surrounded the car. The men moved quietly round to the back. They stared hard at Alec, flushed with annoyance, and observed Meli's restraining hand on his arm.

At Robin's seat, they stopped. 'What ails the lad?' asked a short man with a deep scar on his cheek.

Meli spoke softly. 'His leg is broken; he has much pain and we are trying to get him to Dublin for an operation.' They were words, which had not been used before in Robin's hearing. With another searching look at Alec, the three men put down their rifles.

'Put another bottle up Dad, and we'll have a match.' Robin produced his most disarming smile. 'Oh Dad, please.' Again Meli's fingers tightened on Alec's arm. Meekly, he stepped from the car taking with him Robin's empty ginger-ale bottle. In the ditch, the three men grubbed for pebbles and to Robin they handed the largest.

Scarcely was Alec back at the car when Robin's first stone shot from the back seat. Again it fell short. Wide went each following stone. Meli smiled as she caught the eye of the tall man. Whoever they were, and whatever their business, he was the leader. As Robin opened the second round, the scarred man gently propped him up with his arm. Clang! The bottle flew to pieces. Delightedly Robin tried to jump up in his seat, only to collapse with a moan.

The tall man beckoned Alec to the side of the road, while Meli and the scarred man comforted Robin. The third stood at a discreet distance from the car, listening always and now gently stroking his rifle.

Alec was politely but carefully cross-examined. What were they were really doing on this road? How had they crossed the mined bridge and how had they passed the 'look-out' back at the crossroads?

During his war years, Alec had been arrogant and stubborn, but here in his own gentle countryside the quiet respect of his inquisitor disarmed him. The brogue he knew and understood softened his resentment. Quietly, he explained his anxiety over his son's misfortune. Modestly, he confessed that it was his own rashness which had caused the accident. The tall man mellowed also – for the Irish love their children. He explained that much toil had been spent to fell those great trees, but it had been done to keep 'the Military' in their barracks. At any moment they themselves could have been mown down for what they had done. The Black and Tans had sown hatred and fear throughout the land.

To turn back, Alec explained, would only increase Robin's pain and yet here was the main road to Dublin – the only one for very many miles – blocked and impassable.

The tall man stroked his chin, then called quietly: 'Mick'.

From Robin's side walked scarred Mick. The two men wandered a few steps from Alec and held a whispered conversation. Meli watched anxiously, unable to hear what passed between them. Slowly, Alec walked back to the car, followed after a few seconds by the two men. 'Reverse your car and follow us!' The crisp instruction was an order.

As the tall man raised his hand, his 'guard' opened the rusty iron gate, where shortly before had stood Robin's bottles. The leader walked ahead and Alec slowly followed. Rain had fallen recently and mud lay thick in the field. The car slithered from side to side in the rough cart track which ran along inside the hedge. Slowly, they passed each tree stump until they came to a dip where the track went through a gap in the hedge. Here the car sank into a quagmire and the wheels spun round helplessly. There was nothing Alec could do; each time he accelerated, the car went only deeper in the mud.

In silence, the three men trudged into the slime and put their shoulders to the back of the car. Up to their ankles they pushed, but to no avail. The tall man removed his shabby coat and placed it under the back wheels. He smiled: 'It's for the little lad,' he muttered shyly.

'God bless you,' Alec replied. He let in the clutch very gently and, helped by a mighty shove, the car floated on to the grass. Ahead, the cart track was firmer; some gravel had recently been thrown upon it. As the car gathered speed, he saw ahead the open gate leading back to the road. He dared not stop for fear of getting bogged once more, but once out on the road he pulled up and jumped from the car to give his thanks. No one was to be seen and all was silent. They had gone as silently as they had come, those mysterious but kindly men. God grant them safety from unfriendly bullets, was Alec's heartfelt wish.

To an uneasy Dublin

The barrier of trees cast its spell of silence on the road ahead and for several miles they drove without seeing life or activity. At last, the outskirts of what had formerly been a garrison town appeared. Groups of quiet men lent against the white-washed walls of the thatched cottages, while their black-shawled women stood in darkened doorways. A few bare-legged children mingled with mongrels in the gutters. Over all hung the heavy sweet scent of charred wood. Alec drove on as in a dream, and before long stopped face-to-face with the cause of this tense atmosphere – so charged with the mixture of guilt and determination. In front stood the blackened shell of that once proud barracks, which for generations had housed the forces of the British Crown. Now only wisps of smoke curled up amongst the ruined walls from the highest of which gently fluttered a simple flag – the emblem of freedom, its colours green and orange.

It was the rusty barbed wire, twisted and distorted by the fires' heat, that brought Alec back to reality. For several moments – in themselves timeless and eternal – he had seen Meli standing on those imposing steps, the dawn breaking on her white dress. His jaw set, as it had in the trenches of the Somme. Crisis was all around him. On every side the foundations of his world was being shaken. Paradox climbed on paradox. Here was his country, its soil rich with the smell of bog and fen, tearing itself asunder and dying in front of his eyes. Its great trees felled, roads blown up, destroyed. Before him lay a tortured blackened carcase, stronghold of an occupying power, whose continual might had guaranteed their stability until it was accepted – almost. To this stability Alec had readily given his allegiance in the dark days of 1914. The woman at his side, his wife, was of that power – now challenged, mocked and insulted. What could the future hold against this charred epitaph of superiority? For his boy, not yet out of childhood, the future was dark indeed.

There beats inside the heart of every Irishman a throb so deep that its origin can come only from a past, clouded by echoes, their call speaking of sadness and defeated ambition, of Wolf Tone, of Parnell and O'Connell, of the nameless ones, lost in the mists of time. Alec gazed at this blackened tombstone and knew not whither lay the right or wrong. He had no heart to heed the town's gossip – a further challenge to his loyalties. The car quietly, as from a graveside, slid past the silent group of men and women, out on to the open road, towards Dublin. What lay ahead, only the good Lord knew.

Dublin – Fair Maid of Ireland – sat astride the River Liffey, whose waters, gleaming and fresh within a mile or two of the City, became changed to a dubious hue as they passed under its many fine bridges.

Pride of Georgian architects and home of the eighteenth-century elite, its beautifully proportioned houses, with their fan-lighted entrances, now in whole areas housed hordes of penniless and hungry rabble. The carved front doors had long since during cold, wet winters, been chopped up for firewood; and on the marble steps, once scoured white, sat groups of black-shawled women, their ragged children – urchins indeed – playing or fighting upon the pavements.

These sights, when she came upon them, shocked and saddened Meli as she took her daily walks through the Dublin streets later that June. Robin's leg was mending fast and he was enjoying life in a kindly nursing home. This was situated in one of the big squares that had not fallen to the tenement dwellers. The spacious rooms with their Adam ceilings, the generous windows, the delicately woven iron stair railings, they all spoke of an age of grace and elegance, when Dublin had been one of the world's centres of culture and the arts. So many of the famous names of history had been proud to reside in this gentle and easy-going city on the banks of the Liffey.

The main thoroughfares were crowded, indeed over-full to be healthy or so it appeared to those who knew Dublin in former years. At every street corner stood groups of men, their dark and shabby clothes not speaking of prosperity nor even showing marks of physical toil. Since the end of the Great War, times had been ever harder for the great numbers of men released from war service. In those days, home industry was almost negligible and, for centuries, the industrial needs of Ireland had been provided by an England across the sea. Danger lurked amongst these groups of frustrated and disillusioned men, many of whom had been trained to use the weapons of war at a tender age. As they stood watching, English army lorries rattled by, filled to overflowing with 'the Military'. The city was also strangely full of civilians, whose clothes and accents were not of the Irish soil. True these men were anxious to commence each sentence with 'Begorrah', or 'Bejebbers', but this was only to allay suspicion, for they were representatives of Whitehall's Intelligence Department and many an Irishman knew it. To counteract this 'invasion', murder clubs were being set up throughout the country, and already groups were being formed in lonely back streets and country ditches.

As Meli walked through this once beautiful city, feeling the atmosphere loaded and ominous, she prayed to herself that

Robbie's leg would not delay him long from the calm security of Merlin. Alec, leaving her comfortably installed in the flat of an old friend, had returned several days before and it had been agreed that she would take the mail-boat and visit her parents in England when Robbie was well enough to be collected by Alec. To help the boy keep cheery, he had given him a fishing rod; not the simple kind for catching perch and bream – the common river fish – but a real trout rod, which might even land a fine salmon one day. Alec still fretted over the accident and in this he was not helped by Meli. She had become colder of late and he felt a lack of enthusiasm for everything he did. Her devotion to Robin was touching, but he realised it filled, for her, a vacuum – an ever widening gap between them.

The war had lasted too long and had hardened natures such as Alec's. This he knew and was helpless to change, but what of Meli? Protected and undisturbed by the ravages of that war which had torn the world apart, safe within the silken cocoon of Merlin, her heart, shaped as a gentle rose-bud at their courting, had withered before the full flower had opened; or, if it had opened, Alec had not been at hand to know its fragrance.

Homecoming

Merlin's greeting was as always: the damp lawns smelling of the black soil which lay beneath; ducks and hens fighting over their evening corn. Sadly came the cry of the curlew from a clump of rushes where the river flowed on ... and on. Smoke rose from Merlin's tall chimneys, pale blue in the evening sun; turf from the bog cost nothing, but the world itself could not buy it. Here beat the heart of Ireland, on the surface remote from the storm clouds gathering in far-off Dublin. The evening sky was filled with feathered wisps of golden glory, and the rose hues of the setting sun lit their stems with the gentle touch of a Murillo painting.

At the foot of the grey stone steps, Con O'Toole, tall, thin and worn, though only twenty-three, removed his cap. His eyes burned with happiness; for life – his life – had returned to Merlin. As his master stepped from the car, out tumbled also Robin, the little boy who had meant so much to him in recent years.

In the weeks of Robin's absence, Con, the simple youth, a tenant of great Merlin, had changed more than he dared to realise. Each day, during the long summer of 1920, had strengthened the bands of resistance against the bondage of suppression. Centuries of an unaccepted overlordship were being rolled back by the diehards and fanatics, and in their wake came Con; for Con was ensnared in the 'Fight for Freedom', so soon to echo round the world of those that cared and to be written off by the rest in a masterpiece of understatement as 'the troubles'. Con had been recruited by Martin McCarthy.

On this July evening, however, the life Con had known returned as a tidal wave. Joyfully, he pulled off the suitcases and then accompanied the master in the car to the garage. So little Robbie was well once more and the road from Dublin had been covered in under four hours. Many ruined bridges had been crossed with the aid of the two stout planks tied over the mudguards; but what matter, for during summer time the rivers were low and all travellers got used to the yawning voids below.

Mr. Alec, he noticed, had softened of late, but his bluster, kindly though it was, made Con nervous and awkward. As they walked together from the garage to the back door which led to the kitchen, his master spoke in confidence.

'Con, I know you are really fond of the boy. Therefore, I must tell you of our plans for his future. Here, it is lonely for him and he has few playmates of his own age. Just outside Dublin, there is a good boarding school, which I re-visited yesterday. Odd to think that I myself, at Master Robbie's age, was taken there by my mother twenty-five years ago! The headmaster has promised to take the boy next September; it will be good for him to start and build his future. He will learn more than Miss Livingstone can teach him and he will have the company of other boys.'

Con's heart felt cold, as he said: 'Shure Sir, and it will be fine for the little lad.' Now he was to lose one of his few friends. Con, the youth, cramped by Ed, his practical elder brother, had known so little of life. In the secluded surroundings of Merlin, he had done his manual work day by day. Always he felt tired and weak and prayed to lose that miserable cough which so often made him low and helpless. As he cut the fire logs or cleaned the stables, life seemed useless, but then sometimes little Robbie would appear, bubbling with enthusiasm over his latest curiosity.

'Con, your hand please. I must climb that straw because I know the old red hen has made a nest on top.' Or 'Con, please get the ladder, so I can see if the swallows really have re-built their nest on that rafter.' Now the master's words poured ice over his heart – a cold shroud to his feelings. The little lad would leave Merlin and with him would go the warmth which Con had come to rely upon, more than he realised, in these recent months. They had reached the back door, through which came the house dogs followed by Mrs. Murphy, Merlin's faithful cook, her arm round Robin.

'Oh, Sir! 'Tis good to have the dear lad back,' she called, pressing him to her white apron.

In the dark shadows stood Con, so soon to be alone once more. Dublin he had never even visited. It was the end of the world and beyond to him and there would go that breath of sunshine, embodied in a small fair-haired boy, whose boundless energy and enthusiasm had kept the chill bog mists from entering his own frail body.

As his master went through the old kitchen door, Con heard a soft call – the Curlew call – uttered not by bird but man. This call had recently been adopted by the Resistance, since it was unlikely to raise any suspicion among those who were not meant to know its significance. As he tensed to those appealing notes, he realised that what is taken away is replaced. The door shut out the warm bright light and, as Con turned, he faced the ethereal twilight of an Irish summer's night. All was silent and, as he walked back across the yard, he felt sure that either he had imagined the familiar notes, or indeed it had been a lone curlew crossing the night sky towards the reeds on the river bank. At the large cowshed, however, his blood ran cold. The notes were repeated, but this time from within the shed. No curlew had sought refuge in a cowshed Con knew only too well. A slight rustling inside brought him back to reality. Con himself had taken the cows, after milking, out to the four-acre field. No cattle stayed in overnight during the summer. As if drawn by a magnet, he walked through the door. Inside inky darkness surrounded him. He stood quite still and waited. The hand, which stretched out to grip his shoulder, was firm and the voice that whispered in his ear familiar.

'Con boy, now "himself" is back we'll meet no more at the Lodge. Tonight it's up yonder on the bog, beyond the Cantys' house where the steep face rises. To yer left is a cut; follow it on through the heather and you'll hear the curlew beneath yer boots. Stop where y'are and the ground will open fornent' ye. Step down when yer told, and there take yer orders.' The grip relaxed and a shadow slid out of the low shed.

Mrs. Murphy led Robin to the range on which rested saucepans, their lids hiding the good things within. Alec, the restless Irishman, who had spent long months in the battleground of Western France surrounded by the dark smell of death, warmed his hands by the fire, as he watched the boy's excitement at his welcome. By tradition, the kitchen entrance was the key to a good dinner and Mrs. Murphy was not slow to show her feelings if the master ignored her welcome and preferred the grey stone steps of the front entrance.

'Master Robbie, you're well again. Show us the poor leg, come now there's me darlin'.' The two kitchen maids tittered with awe as Robbie produced his leg for Mrs. Murphy's inspection.

To their surprise there was nothing to see, so well had the hospital's work been done. 'But, then shure hasn't Dublin the finest doctors and all them 'specialising fellers' in the world,' said Maggie Murphy proudly afterwards.

The long passage, leading from the kitchen department towards a green baize door through which was the dining room, was bright with light and Robin was quick to react to this compliment being paid to his home-coming. Merlin possessed a complicated system of petrol gas, which was motivated by a fascinating little engine containing wheels and weights and even a little gasometer. This rose and fell, according to the pressure generated by the hard-working engine, and the whole system was run on high octane fuel. Installed in 1912, the little engine had puffed away merrily until the Great War had thrown its black wings across the peaceful world. Then the appetite of the Royal Flying Corps demanded every drop of high quality petrol available. So through the years Merlin had become used once more to the oil lamp of yesteryear and only on occasions of importance did the little engine have the opportunity to huff and puff its way through the evening. These occasions were so rare that they seemed to give an air of extravagance, with bright lights glistening down the long corridors. From the lawns outside, the spectacle was special, for Merlin dozed in a countryside where time made little change.

During the eighteenth century, many fine and often magnificent houses had been built throughout the land. Labour was abundant and cheap – a very few pence a day. The incomes of the aristocracy, and those wishing to be part of it, were often vast – in some cases £100,000 a year. With such a ratio – incredible by modern standards – the potential was limitless. Vast houses with sixty or more bedrooms, with equally ambitious terraces and formal gardens filled with fountains and surrounded by clipped hedges, were designed by imported Italian architects. Adam ceilings and fireplaces abounded in houses far from centres of society. Distances were of no importance in that heyday of elegant living, and many of the great houses of Ireland were nursed by the willing, if largely inexperienced, hands of as many as fifty servants.

The terrible famine of 1845 reduced the country's population from eight million by a million, with a further two million emigrating. The despair, poverty and gloom that then overhung the land encouraged many of the Anglo-Irish landlords to abstain from residing on their Irish estates. Their English or Continental possessions revolved on a happier note, and thus the term 'absentee' came into the local vocabulary – a term which contained all the hurt feelings of the native population, whom famines had carried beyond the frontiers of starvation and disease. Locally employed Irish agents were given the task of extracting rents from tenants, whose livelihood and ability to toil had diminished to the lowest ebb. Evictions were nationwide and these caused a bitterness so deep that succeeding generations could not forget it. Whole districts were emptied by starvation and emigration. When Liverpool and other British ports became swamped by hordes of desperate immigrants, ships of dubious sea-worthiness appeared in western Irish ports. From Galway, ragged and emaciated families gave, willingly, what little they had left, to escape the despair of their native shores in the hope of a better life in the New World. Statistics sadly prove the small proportion of voyagers who lived to see the promised land.

All this was long ago and now, as Robin stood with Nellie and Phoebe, Merlin's eighteen-year-old housemaids, on those lawns that had seen the carriages of one and a half centuries drive past, the old house beamed forth its radiance. From many of its windows came the warm glow, making it seem so large and young. This was the first time that either of the girls had seen modern gas light. The soft lamps of Merlin and the candles of their roadside cottage were but memories on this special night – a summer's night in 1920.

Barracks ablaze

As Con pushed open the Gate Lodge door, his mother was sweeping crumbs from the kitchen table. She and Ed had already finished their supper, but the coarse cheese and cottage bread remained. Two candles flickered with the draught from the open door. Con, nervous and uneasy, could have put his mother's constant fretful questions to one side, but the sight of Ed sitting in the chimney corner made his heart beat faster. His embarrassment was twofold: for not only was he already overdue at the meeting, but he would have to deceive his elder brother, so gentle and patient, who had always treated him kindly.

Ed's nature stemmed from an infinite past, from which the sufferings and broken ambitions endured by his ancestors had blessed him with a tolerance and a simple code of right and wrong. Ed had never looked for trouble, or courted danger. The village school had given him its paltry best. He read the papers when they were passed on from the big house and he could add the shillings and pennies together for his mother. At fourteen, he started work in the yard at Eila House, Alec's mother's home. Happy days were those for Ed; they never passed without event. The young ladies would need their horses saddled for a meet. 'Ready by 6.30 a.m., please Ed, because it's fifteen miles to Ashburn Cross.' Or Master Alec would be off in his steam car to see that shameless Miss Ponsonby – the blonde one who lived over at Fairlawn – and wanted the steam up at 8 a.m. Why indeed thought Ed, until Master Alec complained that at the bottom of the hill before

Fairlawn Gate, he had to climb down to the stream which flowed beneath the little bridge and collect fresh water for the engine. Just how long it took to raise the steam again, Ed rightly discovered. So life had flowed on full, eventful, but narrow.

At Master Alec's wedding, Madam – Mrs. Casemond of Eila House – had said that Ed must go with him; and so without question, Ed had agreed. The new mistress, whom he had only seen on her visit to Eila House in 1908, was different from anybody he had known. She was 'foreign' in so many ways: she spoke with an accent, was reserved, quiet and, he thought, cold into the bargain. As time went on she had other friends visit her and Ed began to realise that they too were different. Punctuality seemed very important and oh! the fuss over cleanliness. Poor Ed was for ever cleaning out the dog-cart, polishing shoes and sweeping out stables. He often wondered, in his few quiet moments, whether the horses really cared.

With the War and Mr. Alec's departure to the Front, Ed was forced into a new role. He became 'the man of the house'. The young madam – so different from the 'old one' – was now alone with a small boy not yet three years old and a house full of servants, which included that English demon known as Nanny.

As he drove his master to the railway station, Alec told him that the security of the house and all within it rested on his simple shoulders. With the purchase of Merlin three years later, so close to Eila House, Ed was back in his own territory. The Gate Lodge had brought tears of joy from his mother. That frail woman had never dreamed of a house of her own with a slate roof, a real parlour, which she never used, and two bedrooms.

Long years of war, where Ed had been the confidant of his young mistress on so many occasions, had taught him her real worth. That she was different could not be altered, but she was kind and generous. His two sisters – now in America with an aunt – had fared particularly well. Clothing of all kinds had found their way to the Lodge, often by Madam's own hands as she passed through the open gates on her way to the village shop. On her return, food would be placed on the doorstep, if Mrs. O'Toole was not there to receive it.

The master, on his infrequent visits of leave, would slap Ed on the shoulder: 'So, you haven't let the place fall to bits, as I feared! Good lad, it's a comfort to think of you taking care of it all, while I sit in those bloody trenches hearing the rats trying to gnaw their way through my rations.'

Ed looked at Con and did not like what he saw. Was this just the boy's state of health, or was it more? As Con ripped the loaf, which was still hot from the griddle, Ed worried more. Con's face was flushed and he avoided both his mother's eyes and his own. Ed quietly cleaned Con's black boots.

'When I see them lights poppin' through the windows, I fancy how a city like Dublin must look,' said Con.

'It's fine alright, but the folks up there are restless and troubled,' replied Ed.

Con poured more of the strong black tea, which was brewed twice a day and lived on the hearth in a heavy earthenware pot. His hand shook as he did so. He drank it down in a gulp and rose from the table. 'Willie Murphy has a calf that's sick and he asked me to look in and see to it for him.'

'Con, sit now by the fire and be easy,' said his mother. 'There is mist up on the bog and you know it is bad for your chest.'

'Ah! whist to you, mother. It's hot in here and the walk will do me good. Wasn't I heaving dung from the cowsheds all day and me lungs is full of ammonia.' Con went to the door, opened it and then looked back. His eyes were large and dilated. 'To listen to the pair of ye I could still be a wee gossoon!' He smiled, shut the door and was away.

At the outer fence, he paused for fear Ed might follow him, for Willie Murphy was also a friend of his. The kitchen door remained closed and Con's heart started to beat loud and fast. He was now, according to the old clock on the kitchen wall, nearly an hour late, but generally his mother kept it twenty minutes fast, in order that her boys would be in good time for work in the morning. As he reached the bog, the mist met him like a shroud. Wisps eddied up from the warm spongey ground.

To a stranger, terror might be forgiven in these awesome surroundings, but to Con it was his home. The fear he felt was not from these mists or dykes filled with black water but in the cold clamp that imprisoned his heart as he wove his way across the great endless bog that was the backbone of Ireland. The Cantys' house was dark as he passed it. This at least saved more wasted time in chatter. Here now was the steep face and with ease he found the path up to it. At the top, he paused for breath; always he found he wanted to cough after any exertion, but tonight of all nights he knew he dare not. Almost choking he stumbled along the cut. The mist clung heavy and he was quite alone. He stood still, his heart pounding. Was he dreaming? Those bright lights from the big house and Master Robbie's laugh joined with the giggles of Nellie and Phoebe seemed so much more real than that strong hand upon his shoulder. Quite near something stirred; then silence. Con waited. The seconds passed. Almost beneath his boots, the muffled cry of the curlew sounded.

''Tis me, Con O'Toole,' was all he could think of saying. The bog moved and a soft gleam of yellow light climbed up the wall of mist. It moved again to reveal a hole about four feet wide. In the shaft of light was a man's head and shoulders.

'Step down after me,' said a voice unknown to Con.

A ladder took him down into a cavern, hollowed out from the soft turf. A stable lantern set upon the floor threw grotesque shadows on the faces of the assembled company. A haze of blue smoke and the dank smell of wet mackintoshes were symbols that would stay in Con's mind for all time.

'What ailed you Con, Boy?' Martin's voice spoke quietly from behind the haze.

'The Master and the youngun came from Dublin and all the gas jets were put on to greet them. Wasn't that me brother's orders? Admirin' them out there on the lawn we were till dark and after.'

There was an ugly silence and Con felt a shiver run down his back. Did they not believe him? Was he on trial as a traitor?

Martin stepped through the haze and put his hand on Con's thin shoulder. Again his calm voice of authority: 'The gossoon is new to us yet. He doesn't rightly know the rules. He will. I'll teach him.' Then in a tone of command: 'To business, me lads, there's no time to waste. We're late already. Kevin here has just come from Dublin. Come Kevin, tell us what you know about the new visitors to Ireland.'

A youth from Rynah, whom Con had only seen once before, stepped forward, stamped out a cigarette butt and cleared his throat. 'The City's full of them. And a more miserable crowd of mongrels you never saw. Tall, short, fat and scrawny and not even a decent uniform amongst them. Some has black pants and tan jackets and others the reverse. But there's one thing they all have in common and that's murder in their eye. They're the scum of the British jails and a more wicked-looking lot of bastards you never set eyes on.' Kevin spat on the peat floor and continued.

'Our own H.Q. intercepted the news that these fine customers, who would rape yer mother and rob the graveyard of its corpses, are to be installed in any empty police barracks throughout the country.' An inward drawing of breath signified the dismay of ten men gathered beneath the ageless Irish turf.

'What are the instructions, Kevin?' asked a voice from the shadows.

'Martin here's in charge and the target is Rynah.'

There was a shuffling of nervous excitement in the cavern. Here then was the first real action for this part of the country. Further south, private houses had been raided and burned by both British and illegal Republican forces. The British censored press admitted to nearly 6,000 raids by the winter of 1919. In March 1920, Thomas MacCurtain, Lord Mayor of Cork, had been murdered during the night in front of his wife and children. The Coroner Jury's verdict stated: 'Wilfully murdered under circumstances of most callous brutality: the murder having been organised and carried out by the Royal Irish Constabulary, officially directed by the British Government.' Members of the R.I.C. had started to resign their commissions in large numbers, but the Republican Secret Service, powerful and widespread, had responded in kind: they struck terror by ambushes, propaganda and social ostracism. Many police barracks lay empty and deserted. The remaining members of the R.I.C. – mostly elderly men awaiting pensions – had moved into the larger towns, where barracks and army H.Q. were fortified and surrounded by barbed wire.

Although Kevin's news brought excitement, it also brought a sober reality to the minds of those present. They were about to burn to ashes the Rynah Police Barracks, empty these past few months; but the Barracks were the property of the 'Authorities', who took their orders from London. Already severe punishments were being meted out by steel helmeted British troops for any infringement of the law, but once Government property was interfered with, then the ones responsible and even sometimes their innocent relatives were 'on the run'. By a cunning drafting of the law, a man on the run became an outcast. Anyone harbouring him, or even giving him food or assistance, was himself guilty in the eyes of the law.

Rynah was a small village and the barracks building stood at the edge of it on the road which led to Ardmore.

At the edge of the bog, hidden behind a ditch, the men had concealed their bicycles. So strict was the secrecy of their rendezvous that Con, the newcomer, for fear of giving suspicion to Ed, had not been told to bring his. Martin, his sponsor, however, had brought a second one, and as they covered the few miles of empty road he spoke softly to him.

'Above all, lad, don't get caught! If we're surprised and surrounded, run for it. Hide where you can until the search passes. If they catch you, there'll be any means used to get information out of you. The lives of all of us are at risk. Guard your tongue!'

As had been agreed in the bog cavern, the men stopped at an old ruined barn, which occasionally sheltered sheep in heavy winters. The floor was strewn with straw, which a critical observer might have noticed was new. Underneath, four cans of petrol had been hidden that same afternoon. A pale moon shone on the men as they left the barn, some carrying straw under their arms, others the petrol cans under their raincoats. Irish villages of those days went to bed early; electric light had not yet reached them. Within a hundred yards stood the police barracks, gaunt and empty. The moon's reflection on the few unbroken window panes emphasized its bleak outline. As they walked slowly up to the building all was quiet; the only sound was the pounding of each man's heart. A group of Irish yew trees inside the gate was their assembly point and, as they stood in silence, the eerie cry of the curlew came from the back of the

barrack building. This was their signal and each man knew
from his briefing in the bog cavern what his duty must be.

A rough drawing of the building had been shown under the
lantern's yellow glow. The back door lay open and in slipped
Con with three other men. Nervous excitement made his
cheeks burn and his breath came harder. For this, his first
assignment, he must, on a signal from the upper floors, grope
his way through the ground floor rooms, pouring petrol as he
went. As each floor was set alight, the men would take to the
stairs with all speed and only when they were safely by the
open door could Con light his bundles of petrol-soaked straw.
As he waited, he heard the footsteps above. Would their work
ever be complete? Outside, he knew that Martin guarded their
escape route through a small wood which led to the open fields.

At last, two thumps sounded from the top floor, followed
by a crackling as the ignited straw burst into a blaze. Hurried
footsteps announced the arrival of the first men to the floor
above Con. Already he could see from the stairwell the
changing lights of the fire. Now louder footsteps over his head
were followed by the crackle which brought the fire nearer.
Con's hands shook as he held the match box which was to
ignite his own tinder box. Only one flight of stairs separated
him from his mates and the deathly flames. Three quick thuds
on the ceiling above his head were mingled with the roar of a
motor car. Headlights shone brilliantly through the broken
window where Con stood. Time stopped. The match shook as
he tried to strike it. Now all was confusion. Boots clattered
down the single flight of stairs followed by gusts of rancid
smoke, burning straw, petrol and old timber. Outside voices
were raised in querulous demand. As Con's match flickered to
life, he counted three silhouettes in the confused lights of the
moon, car headlights and a thick yellow haze from the
staircase. He threw it into the bundle of straw, only a few feet

from where he stood. A blinding burst of flame lit the empty room and sped down the path created from his petrol can. Instinctively, he followed his instructions, numb even to the shouting voices which had not been part of his briefing. As a rat from a burning haystack, he fled through the open door. In the clear night air, shots sounded only yards away, and a groan nearby made his blood run cold.

'Lads, run for your lives, live to fight again!' The words were Martin's and as they ended they were followed by the voice of Colonel Kernahan, Squire of Ardmore Castle.

'Rats, bastards! We'll get the lot of you!'

The glare from the now blazing building mingled with the car headlights and gave Con his first nightmare picture of the Revolution. He ran towards the haven of the little wood and there, only by falling in the thick undergrowth could he avoid the brilliant glare which lit the countryside. As he crawled through the bracken, he waited for a shot to halt his journey. It did not come and shouts of frantic men drew away down the road to Rynah. His heart thumped and his head ached with the fumes of burning timbers filling his nostrils. 'Get away at all costs.' Martin's words rang in his ears. Stealthily, he slid through the undergrowth towards the open field. There he lay until the car lights turned back towards the village. 'Oh God!' thought Con, 'Which of us is the fox for this hunt to the death?'

At last, he felt it was safe to climb from the undergrowth and stand up once more. His shirt was damp with sweat and yet he dare not cough to clear his throat. As he crossed the field, the glare of the fire was shielded by the wood. 'God bless it!' thought Con. 'Thanks be to God for His protection.'   For a long time, he sat hidden by the tall hedge. He longed to calm his nerves with a Woodbine but dared not light another match. The first had created enough havoc. The night grew cold and the moon was already low. If he kept to the hedge, he might be safe. What had befallen Ireland, the soft and gentle land of his birth? Must freedom always be so hard to win?

The groan that Con had heard came from young Kevin, the Rynah youth who had brought the news from Dublin of the arrival of the Black and Tans. Martin too had heard his cry of pain as the master of Ardmore charged after his prey. Plunging through the smoke, he stumbled mercifully over the fallen lad. Not sparing a second to ask the source of his pain, Martin grabbed the writhing body and slung it over his broad shoulders. When Kernahan fired again, some shot rattled against Martin's raincoat, but the main impact fell wide of its target. Now Martin felt he was marked, but the increasing fire, fanned by a slight breeze, threw a shield of protective smoke in his direction. The straw had done its work efficiently and Martin used this to make his escape. He had paid many secret visits to the empty barracks buildings of late, and he well knew that escape from ambush meant freedom; otherwise it would be captivity – even death. A shed at the far end of the yard must be reached to give temporary shelter and, as luck would have it, the breeze was blowing increasing banks of smoke in that direction. Slowly, he stumbled towards the shed, his lungs filled with foul fumes, but he knew that if he fell Kevin would suffer greater pain and would not be able to control his cries. By day, Martin had not realised how wide the yard would seem, but he knew that somewhere in the middle was an old well. He prayed quite simply and Kevin heard the muttered words as he clung helplessly to his hero. He had always admired Martin, but now he knew what a leader and friend this strong man had become. The thud as Martin's body bumped against the shed wall made the pain so great that Kevin sobbed into Martin's ear.

'God help us Martin! They got me in the leg.'

'Whist lad,' came the answer, 'or they'll get you again on the next round.' He picked his way round to the back of the shed and pushed open the door, carefully left ajar early that morning. Equally carefully he had seen to it that there was a large heap of straw in the far corner. How far-sighted he had been he now knew, for the chances of getting Kevin away immediately were negligible. More cars had arrived and outside all was chaos. The villagers had streamed forth to see the blaze and someone was shouting through the smoke that the well must be found for water. Gently, he laid Kevin down on the edge of the straw and quickly pulled away the back of the mound. Purposely he had left the straw loose for such an emergency. In a few seconds he made a burrow into which he laid Kevin, then covered him over. How many wanted men and women had sheltered in straw before this?

'Be easy now me boy, they'll not find you if you stay good and quiet. I'll be back for you as soon as this blasted mob moves away. You never know who's your friend in a crowd like this. That murderous Kernahan and his bloody gun mustn't find you again tonight.'

Kevin's hand closed round Martin's arm: 'You're a fine man, Martin, and I always said so. With the likes of you we'll free the country. Thanks man.' The fingers loosened and the youth relaxed into the soft sweet smelling straw.

Behind the shed was a dyke; it was full in the winter but now only a trickle went through it. Deep enough to hide a man. Martin slid down the bank. The dark mud smelt good after the stench of burning timber.

From nearby Kahirloch streamed a line of military trucks, their acetylene headlamps glaring through the dark night. By releasing shrapnel on the lonely country roads, they hoped to disperse the all too frequent ambushes by a rapidly organising I.R.A. Merlin's part of Ireland still slept in the past and actually the Military had little to fear. As they passed the Gate Lodge, Con's mother rose from her bed and pulled aside the thin net curtains. Trouble was abroad and she shivered. Where was it leading Ireland? Her flock had diminished from the days when her large brood filled their small house. Ed and Con were her life now and Con was delicate. Of late, he had become silent. His cheeks bore a constant flush. He came late to their frugal evening meal. Ed, as always, fretted over his work and responsibility at Merlin, details of which his mother knew too well. What was Con's life, though? What thoughts ran through that fertile mind? And these worries often overwhelmed her. Of course, he had gone as he said to help Willie Murphy with his sick calf, but here it was past midnight and she had not heard the latch on the back door.

The military only moved by night when trouble roamed the gentle countryside. Towards Rynah they sped now, throwing up clouds of dust from the unpaved road. Why to Rynah which lay a bare three miles to the west and where she as a young colleen had been born those long years ago, when Parnell had spoken well for Ireland at the Parliament of Westminster? He had failed to convince them but he had helped nurse the pain which was Ireland. Politics meant little to a peasant woman, and her sons derived their livelihood from Merlin. The smoke from its chimneys meant continuity of life through her sons. Master Alec she respected, for he stood for security to her family and many more on the estate. He waved when he passed the Gate Lodge and his smile was loved in the whitewashed cottages which lined the boreens of Tipperary. The lady was different. Her voice was quiet and gentle; she had said little, but her words were sincere. When either Nora or Katie had been sick, 'the Missus' had been quick to visit the Gate Lodge.

With her she brought needed things: warm clothing, Merlin's honey for the sore chest, a packet of Lipton's tea, which callers could sip as they came to sit by the peat fire. Then the farewell, the warm pressing of the hand and inside that welcome folded banknote.

Within the hour, Mary O'Toole, shielding herself from the damp mist, would be on her way to Kahirloch. In the village, she would buy from Canty's store oats for the morning porridge, sugar for the tea and then across the street to the butcher, Pat McIntyre, who knew she only wanted the cheap cuts and remnants for the black iron pot, which hung eternally from a chain over the kitchen fire.

She shivered and let the net curtains fall back in place. For no reason, her mind moved to Nora and Katie, safe in Chicago, a city Mary would never see; that was unless the girls married well enough to invite her over to visit them. An unlikely event in 1920, but hope burned in her heart to see America where so many of her own generation had also emigrated. Her sister-in-law had married a Cork man and together they had set up a small shop in Oak Park, a suburb of Chicago. Within a few years, they were able to write to Mary, knowing of her husband's death, asking whether the girls would like to go and live with them. Sadly she had agreed, knowing it was for their own good. Now the occasional dollar bill arrived and this last Christmas a pair of flesh-coloured silk stockings! She would never wear them, but they were treasured and lived in the bedroom cupboard, proudly displayed when any female neighbour called.

Mary O'Toole, widow and mother, picked her way across the room on a pale moonbeam to the trestle bed which filled one corner. Like Ed, her eldest, she feared change to come over this gentle forgotten land.

A casualty is found

During the early summer, Merlin knew almost no night. The pale dawn cast its ethereal but dead whiteness over the sleeping fields. A wren – brave little bird – gave her solo notes. At first, the earth still slept, but she had disturbed the conscience of a blackbird, whose little clearing of the throat allowed her to announce the new day. In its turn, the rest of the bird world closed its ranks and then, as Robin listened from his window, the crescendo glory of the morning chorus filled Merlin's park. Tireless, the cuckoo, who had repeated his beloved call till late into last night, was once again telling of his happiness to be here in the greenness of this tranquil island, far from his southern home. More than one pheasant gave notice of its whereabouts – tame birds, reared by motherly Merlin hens, one day they would rise on the autumn breeze and meet their end through man's lust to destroy.

The song thrush and robin now, from their different trees, vied with each other to lift their song into the golden rays, heralding the coming of the sun. Across the fields the river, a great grey snake, lay still and from its rushes came one by one the calls of coot, grebe and waterhen. Nearer, a plover raised his worried call above the meadows and from the marshy ground came that of the haunting curlew.

From all sides, nature, through her birds, gave welcome and the beauty of their song, so pure and innocent, filled Robin with a gratitude to be part of this glorious world. Although it was not yet four o'clock, and Merlin still slept, he pulled on his clothes. His mongrel, Scam, had heard his step and, as Robin opened the schoolroom door, he jumped from his basket, tail a-wagging. Together they went down the great black bog oak staircase and through a small side door on the east side of the house, then turned down a tree-lined path to the open fields. Bird song was all around them. Scram ran ahead; the early morning smells were his favourites. The path ended in an arch formed by the young oaks, and here Robin waited watching the scene before him. The fields fell away in a gentle slope and then rose again towards Firgrove Hill. From the whole valley, as if drawn by a magic wand, there rose a soft white mist. It sat as a blanket, but of softest fluff, and through it the hedgerows looked suspended – as very long grey destroyers on a calm sea. The kaleidoscope of dawn was turning gently before his eyes. Little by little, the mist evaporated until the hedges were anchored fast to earth once more. Over the tip of Firgrove Hill, something was happening moment by moment – impossible to describe Robin found afterwards but wonderful to witness. The black firs were being moved forward on the horizon to make way for a 'presence'. Robin felt he could see them move and, as he watched, the upper rim of a huge and scarlet sun peeped shyly over the edge of Merlin's horizon. Giant hands were pushing it higher, inch by inch, and with it came a radiance he would never forget.

Along the path, he had picked a bunch of bluebells, smelling so sweetly in the cool morning air. Gently, he laid them at his feet and knelt beside them: 'Dear God, thank you for this great beauty. Thank you for my home and for allowing me to be alive and see and feel all this. Help me to give kindness in return.'

Scram came bounding up, but for once did not jump all over Robin. Instead he stood quite still and smelled the bluebells. As the sun climbed, one lark after another rose from the meadows carrying beautiful notes ever upward to meet the new day.

It would be a long time before Miss Livingstone would expect him to eat his breakfast in the schoolroom. Later he would go and watch Mrs. Murphy build up her fire in the kitchen range. He wandered through the fields where nature lived – it was Robin's world. Up to Firgrove Wood, he and Scram went, up into this new and exciting day. As they entered the wood, flights of pigeons sped from their trees and the pines, which were planted in his Grandfather's time, appeared dark and mysterious. Under a hill in the wood was a big cavern, hollowed out by his father and aunts when they were children, years before. Robin loved this forgotten grotto, and used it as his secret hideout. Inside, was some of his treasure trove which he knew Miss Livingstone would disapprove of: a fox's skeleton, eggs robbed and carefully blown from forbidden birds' nests, a battered piece of his father's earliest electric car. So it is with small boys who love treasures which meet with the disapproval of their elders.

Scram shared the hideout, as he shared much of Robin's life, and bounded forward into the cavern. Always he came out after a few moments to continue his endless sniffing of the forest floor. This time, he remained inside, but Robin could hear the swishing of his tail as he himself entered the cool darkness. At first, he could only blink, for the sun outside shone brightly on this July morning. Then to his surprise, he saw a pile of straw, fresh and yellow on the earthen floor. Upon it lay a dark object which was attracting Scram's attention; Robin's heart beat fast. His father had told him of the exciting events which had taken place here in his childhood, but then Alec Casemond had been one of a large flock; Robin was an only child and many of his games were solitary. On his initial visits he had come here with Miss Livingstone, but now he was a big boy, 8 $\frac{1}{2}$ years old, and this was his stronghold. Who and what had dared transgress the Grotto's sanctity? Robin tried hard not to feel frightened; at least Scram did not seem scared – he did not even bark. Robin went forward through the entrance and, as his eyes became accustomed, he realised that the dark object was a body, a man's body.

'Who are you and what are you doing here?' Robin's voice was a little shrill, with fear or excitement, it mattered little, for the reply came quickly, and from a voice so soft and gentle that it soothed what fear the young boy may have had.

'I'm ill lad, and I think I'll die before the night is out.'

Robin's heart missed a beat; he had no idea what was taking place. Only he felt for the sick man, who sounded like his beloved Con.

'Oh, cheer up. What's wrong with you anyway?' He tried to sound brave.

''Tis me leg, it's broke and hurts like the devil. I'm that parched me throat's afire. Oh boy, could you get me a sup of water and a bite to eat, I'd bless you evermore?' The soft voice trailed off, but Robin was reassured. Whatever the trouble was, he knew it would not hurt him. Furthermore, it was still early and of course he must help.

'I broke my leg sailing a boat and had to go to hospital in Dublin; it hurt very much but I had a good time. Mine was in plaster for weeks, but it kept straight while it mended.' Robin peered forward. He saw no splint, which was how he travelled to Dublin. Oh well, he would think about that as he crossed the fields to Merlin. As he turned to leave, the man's hand gripped his.

'You are Master Robin of Merlin?'

'Yes, of course, who are you?'

Through the same darkness came a sigh. 'Ah lad, I have no name no more, but I'll not hurt you.' As he spoke, his teeth chattered with cold. The cavern was not a place to spend any length of time.

'You're cold, like I was when I broke my leg, and then it hurt much more.' Robin tried hard to bring cheer to his voice. 'I know, I'll try and bring you a blanket. Don't you want anybody to know you are here?' This he had to ask, but as to why this man lay here, cold and sick on a summer's morning, he felt he should not ask.

'God praise you, boy,' said the voice, and Robin thought he detected a sob.

'I'll go quickly now and I'll run all the way across the fields. The larder window may be open and I'll climb in and get some food. I hope Mrs. Murphy won't catch me; she can be awfully fierce.'

Kevin lying in the shadows smiled at the name, his own aunt, safe in the Merlin bosom; if only he dared tell the boy his name, he knew his aunt would open her large heart to his needs. But from Martin he had learnt his lessons: 'Never trust no one.' He had many times repeated: 'In this struggle families will be divided though fear or favour, even by bribery or threats.' How much more dangerous would his secret be in the hands of this small boy, a known product of the aristocracy, and yet he liked the warm frankness with which the lad spoke. He sensed that Robin Casemond was trying to cheer him.

'Go then boy and God go with you. The day may come when I can do a good deed for you.'

The nightmare recalled

As Robin left the cavern followed by Scram, the chill of emptiness returned, so temporarily arrested by that bright chirruping voice. Kevin recalled the nightmare events of the last hours. He had lain under the straw in the barracks shed, listening to the babble of voices and almost suffocated by fumes, as the rising wind blew clouds of smoke across the yard. Maybe he dozed, he did not know, but suddenly he felt his body lifted out of its warm tunnel of straw.

'A cry out of ye and yer a dead man,' whispered Martin in his ear. 'The Military are coming; see there are the lights on the hill yonder. It's now or never more, me boy.' Martin's brains and strength saved them both that night. Within two minutes of their departure from the shed, the burning barracks was surrounded by bright lights from trucks and the shouting voices of soldiers. Martin had laid a concealed plank over the dyke and, after they had crossed it, he kicked it down the slippery bank out of sight of curious eyes. Carrying Kevin as gently as possible across a small field, he reached a ruined farm house. Here in the yard shed stood a donkey, already harnessed in its cart. Again Martin's wisdom triumphed, for he had had the premonition that some casualties must result from this daring exploit. That his employer, James Kernahan, curse his stinking bones, would be so quickly on the spot, with the loaded gun, even Martin had not foreseen; but these were early days and there was still much to be learned. He had never liked the Colonel and, as he gently laid Kevin in the straw-filled cart, he came to hate him more. Arrogant and rude, with an open dislike for the peasantry and their cause, Kernahan had spent many years soldiering in India. To him, Martin's kind were 'the natives' and to be treated as such. Ah well! Time would tell, and what mattered now was to get Kevin to a place of safety, but where was that place? Rynah was impossible – the village street was thronged and surely the military would make a house to house search.

Ardmore, rich in outhouses, was also too dangerous because it would mean passing through part of the village. In his youth, Martin had earned two shillings as a beater for the Merlin pheasant shoots. He knew the woods and copses, and now that the military had come from Kahirloch it might, with God's grace, be safe for an hour or two to use that road for his wanted cargo. A crescent moon lit the way across two large fields. All was silent and serene. Why was this bloodshed, only just begun, necessary to achieve an island's freedom? Martin's education had been scant, but his brain was crystal clear. In the faint moonlight, his white teeth gleamed through a firm-set mouth. Whenever the end should come, it would only come one way – through Victory and Freedom. The road was deserted and, as the donkey ambled on, Kevin lay beneath the straw. To have driven fast would have raised suspicion of any passing motor car. As it was, Martin was just a lone peasant returning late to his cottage. After two miles, he drew level with Merlin's Firgrove Wood. Opposite laid the entrance gate to Dr. Lyster's house. Martin paused there to think seriously where he could deposit Kevin. In his hurry, he had decided on Merlin's Gate Lodge. But now in the calm moonlight he realised this to be impossible. Con had done his work well at the barracks, but had not been seen since. He might be home – or dead. These were bitter times. Ed was not to be trusted: too loyal to his job, too devoted to Merlin and its owners. Martin had respect for Mr. Casemond, which he lacked for his own employer; but then hadn't Mr. Casemond been away in the war fighting for the British Forces and weren't they now the Enemy?

The stillness of the night was disturbed by the distant roar of a motor car. Martin was trapped right there against the doctor's gate. Within moments he was blinded by the lights.

'Kevin, you're a dead man and don't forget it; you'll be deader if there's a sound out of you. I'll handle this.'

The high military truck ground to a halt. 'Hey there! What the hell do you think you're doing? Have you been in Rynah tonight?'

Martin slouched over the reins and hiccupped audibly.

'Have a pity gentlemen,' he whined. 'Aint I on me way to fetch the doctor for me Missus? She's taken with terrible pain.'

'Where do you live?'

'Down there in the bog, and the poor creater moanin' enough to bring tears to me eyes.'

Martin made as if to get down from the cart and open the doctor's gate. There was muttering from the truck and as quickly as the Military had arrived, they departed.

Now Martin had a real problem. He could not be discovered again on this road. He had waved across fields to denote where his wife lay moaning. It was reached by a narrow lane which ran along the side of the doctor's property. From this he could enter Firgrove Wood and, as a light flashes in one's brain, so he remembered the big cavern deep in that wood, where gossip had it the former Casemonds from Eila House used to play as children. What a sanctuary, even if a damp one for poor Kevin, lying so quiet in the back of the cart.

The first rays of dawn were breaking as Martin carried his burden into the dark retreat. He pulled straw from the donkey cart to make a bed and, after he had laid Kevin upon it, he put more over him to try and keep the youth warm. Outside the birds started to sing and in the dawn light, Martin looked down at his clothes. They were stained with mud from the dyke, but worse: large patches of Kevin's blood were on his own coat jacket – the kind of evidence which Colonel Kernahan would dearly like to observe.

'Kevin lad, I'll be back in the evening. God be with you. You're safe here, and many a time our fathers went hungry before us. Lie quiet and help will come to you.'

Kevin, weakened through loss of blood, cold and hungry could only whisper. 'Thanks, Martin. I'll always say – if I live through this – you're a fine man.'

'Of course you'll live! Shure isn't there work to be done? Be easy now me brave gossoon.'

The donkey took him through by-lanes – known in Ireland as 'boreens' – and across fields to the precincts of Ardmore. There Martin tethered the ass and walked to an outhouse where he hung his work clothes. Quickly he changed to start another day.

A secret mission

Robin arrived breathless in the outer yard. He was excited, for now he was on a real secret mission. The stories he read told of heroes who saved pretty girls from wicked robbers, and of strong cowboys who dealt firmly with marauding Indians. But, although he lived the excitement of their escapades, he realised that their reality was doubtful. How many eight-year-old boys had a real live man lying helpless and wounded in their own secret hideout and furthermore dependent on his, Robin's, immediate and speedy action? On his run, he had determined how to solve the problem of food; in addition, he knew where his father's wartime water bottle hung. This he could wash and fill from a drinking tap near the garden door. His real worry was some form of covering for his poor shivering guest. He could, if careful, try to take a blanket from one of the Merlin guest rooms, but his heart failed at the thought of being caught by Nellie or Phoebe as they bustled through the bedroom floors. Automatically, his mind went to Con. He would help and as always solve Robin's problem. From one to another of the yards he sped, not on this occasion daring to call out Con's name. Easily he might be heard and summoned, since it would soon be his breakfast time. To his surprise, Con was nowhere to be found whereas always before on his early morning rambles, he had returned by the stable yard in order to greet his friend and hero. Excitement turned to despair; so much depended on Con now in this vital moment – the first really dangerous secret that Robin had ever held.

Alright, he could at least invade Mrs. Murphy's larder and the sooner the better, for Merlin was awakening fast. The larder window, as he had hoped, was partly open and stealthily he crept through it. There on the cold marble slabs lay partially demolished chickens and a fine roast of beef. This latter he knew he dare not take for it would be missed immediately. Desperate, he grabbed a chicken carcase which had plenty of flesh on it and slid back the open window. At this moment, Mrs. Murphy, unknown to Robin, glanced across the small inner courtyard, and to her amazement saw the young boy slide down on to the grass. She loved him for his gaiety and enthusiasm and so her mind was not really troubled. 'The poor wee creater had,' she guessed, 'been up for many an hour on this glorious morning and it was likely he was by now half starved and his breakfast would not be served for another while yet.'

Robin went round to a small west door which led into the ground floor. Nearby was the gun room, filled with all the sporting gear used by his father: guns, fishing rods, golf clubs, tennis racquets, water bottle. He took down from a wall hook his fishing basket and stuffed in the chicken carcase. Small worry if later it tasted of perch. Although only eight years old, Robin was acutely aware that he was playing an important role in a desperate drama. His life so far had been entirely sheltered as the only child of great Merlin, buried away in this sleepy countryside, loved by indoor and outdoor staff and even Miss Livingstone, who fussed over him like an old hen.

It was now 8 o'clock and he knew that Con must be around. A horrible thought gripped him as he crossed the stable yard. Could Con be ill? He knew that he was delicate, and Robin had often experienced the twinge of terror lest he might be without his bosom friend and confidant. Still unable to call out for fear of being summoned to the schoolroom, he wandered from shed to shed, into the large kitchen garden and on through the flower garden and glasshouses. Robin was in despair. Almost without thinking, he wandered towards an old creaking door which led out through the high garden wall. Outside was a shed where plants for the glass houses were potted up. The potting shed was a favourite hideout of Robin's. By the hour, he used to chat to Con as he filled the earthenware flower pots of all sizes with a rich mixture of dark soil and peat mould. He pushed open the door and looked along the potting counter – no Con. He went round the back of the shed where the pots were stacked and to his intense joy there sat Con on a wooden stool. His head was buried in his hands and he had not even heard Robin coming upon him.

On this warm sunny morning with all the birds singing, this was not the place for Con to be spending his time. Automatically, Robin wanted to jeer at Con for being so lazy, but something made him pause. His friend was shivering. Gently, the boy crept up to the slouched figure and put his hand on the thin shoulder.

'Con, dear Con, what's wrong? I have looked for you everywhere. I've been up since 4 o'clock and I've been to Firgrove Wood and, Con, I've got to talk to you, it's so important.'

As Con looked up, Robin saw how white his cheeks were and he looked into the dark sunken eyes.

'Shure Master Robbie, I'm feeling terrible weak this mornin'. Didn't I have a bad spell of coughin'.' Con had to think and lie quickly, for this small boy must know nothing of his night's ordeal. In a way he wished he could tell him, for it would relieve his troubled mind. But rules were rules and he had been warned against giving away any information, and if he were to do so to a child, his fellow rebels – for he was one of them since last night's work – would show him no mercy.

51

Robin's next outburst nearly caused him to stop breathing.

'Con, I had to find you. Something terrible has happened.' Without pausing, the boy ran on: 'Up in the wood, you know where there's the old cavern, Scram and I found a wounded man. He says he has no name, but he is shivering on a pile of straw, which wasn't there the last time I went; and he has blood on his clothes. I told him that I would get him food and a blanket. Oh Con! He is so cold and sad in there. I think he's frightened there alone and he told me his leg was broken – you know like mine was.'

Proudly Robin showed his fishing satchel. 'Look, see! I've filled Dad's water bottle.' Con's heart missed a beat as the boy told his story. Somehow, he knew that the wounded man must be part of last night. He had heard that cry of pain after the two shots, but smoke had hidden the victim. Many times as he walked back to the Gate Lodge he had wondered which of their number had fallen.

Robin was still talking excitedly: 'We've got to help him, or he may die there in the cold. Shall I go back and try and take a blanket from one of the spare rooms or do you think Phoebe and Nellie will catch me?' So far, this was Master Robbie's plot, but instinctively Con knew that he must somehow join forces with the boy. At the briefing on the bog the previous night, Martin had mentioned nothing of the cavern in the wood and yet Con was convinced that a man who would not give his name, but was lying wounded, must also have been helped to the cavern.

'No, Master Robbie, don't go near the spare rooms. Wait here and I'll slip back to the horse boxes and get a blanket from there.' Con too could be missed from his work and he was now thinking clearly. On the way, he would tell one of the gardeners that he would be busy in the potting shed if needed. Supervision at Merlin was slight and if he let it be known what he intended to do, there was little likelihood of trouble. The Master cared little for the garden and the Missus, who spent much time there, was still away in England. Furthermore, everyone knew Master Robbie's devotion for Con and frequently he would be dragged away from his work to take the boy perch fishing on the river for hours at a time. Robbie was delighted and relieved at Con's idea of the horse blanket – Con solved all their problems.

'I'll wait for you here, but do please hurry back, then I will take everything back to the wood.'

As Con crossed the garden, he called to one of the young lads digging the early potatoes, telling him that he would be potting today. The stables were deserted, since all the horses were out in the fields and it was easy to slip a folded blanket under his arm. By the time he reached Robin, his mind was made up. What the boy knew already could not be helped, but this was man's work. How could Robbie cope with what might be needed in the cavern. 'It's a fine secret you have laddie,' Con spoke as if it were a joke. 'Quite the detective you are to be sure. It can't be many young gossoons who find real live fellas lying wounded in their own hideouts. I'm feeling better now and the walk'll do me good. I'll slip over and see what ails him.'

'But Con, I told him I wouldn't tell anyone. It's all a secret between him and me.'

'Shure and since when did you and I have any secrets between us? And whoever the fella is, he must be a stupid fool. Poaching our young pheasants in the woods I'll be bound and fell and bust his leg. He may need help that you'd be not strong enough to give him.' Con used his ace: 'When I was back now at the yard I could hear Miss Livingstone bawling her head off for you. I didn't let on that I knew where you were, but it's way after time for your breakfast and you know what that one is; she'll be off to the Master with one of her tales.'

He had pricked the boy's bubble and he hated himself for doing so, but what else could he do. He was still much shaken by the night's ordeal, without sleep or food. Maybe there would be enough food for two on that chicken carcase.

'Blast that silly old hag and her fussing,' Robin fumed. 'Anyhow, once I go to school, I won't have her chasing after me next holidays.' This remark in turn hurt Con. What a dull place Merlin would be without this excitable little companion.

'Off you go now, Master Robbie. I'll promise to tell your visitor that these gifts are from you and I'll see to his needs while you get back to your breakfast. When you've finished your lessons, come back to me here; but don't let on what you've been at or they'll raise a stink in the house.'

'Oh alright, but I did want to go with you.' There was such a note of disappointment in his voice that Con almost weakened. In earlier days he would have done so, but last night had hardened his soft heart.

As the boy ran off, frightened now at the prospect of facing his governess, Con picked up the fishing bag and water bottle and over his arm he placed the folded blanket. Walking across the fields, he realised that, innocently, the boy was helping 'the Cause'. To help anyone on the run was a crime, but who would put blame on a child of eight years old especially if he were the son of Merlin? No such luck would fall his way if he were discovered, and he found himself wondering if he had been a fool to implicate himself further, rather than let the boy continue with his own plan. He quickened his pace to match his mounting curiosity as to who this man might be. Robbie had pulled many tricks on him in the past and it was just possible that here was another occasion where he was being ragged – to use the boy's own word – but no, there had been something so sincere in his manner and the ensuing disappointment so acute. Con put his hand under the blanket to pat the fishing bag. That at least was real and to risk Mrs. Murphy's wrath was too high a price to pay for any joke.

As he climbed up into Firgrove, wood pigeons flew from the tall dark trees. He entered the quiet world of the forest. Shafts of sunlight here and there crossed his path. These trees had been strong and tall when the Master and his brothers played here as children. Even the cavern to which he was hurrying was dug long before their day. The cruel flames, the smell of burning straw and timbers all seemed an unreal nightmare here in this serene and harmless world of nature.

Although Con's introduction to mortal danger was not yet twelve hours old, he had the instinct of a peasant and the blood running in his veins had centuries of an ingredient known as self-protection mixed with it. Revolvers had been freely distributed, though from whence they came Con never questioned. These weapons fired quickly in a nervous hand and here, trapped in this cavern, lay a wounded man at bay. To walk straight inside might give cause for regret on both sides. As Con neared the cavern, he softly whistled Danny Boy. At the entrance he stopped, but to one side, safe from a possible revolver bullet. All was silent around him. He had often intended to practise the curlew call; now he needed it. The result was not good and a passing curlew would have been indignant, but after a moment's pause, it brought forth a sigh from within the cavern

'It's Con O'Toole. The boy sent me. He couldn't get back himself. Not that he didn't have his heart breaking, but his teacher was yelling for him. He sent you the food, water and a blanket. He's a grand wee gossoon.'

'For the love of God, Con, come in to me. It's me – Kevin.' Con, confident now, walked in and up to the pile of straw. 'I'm shot, Con. It's me they got and me leg is ruined.'

Con put his hand on the cold forehead: 'Take it easy man. What's in a leg? There's worse might have beset you. Who brought you here?'

As Kevin told his story, the two men tore apart Mrs. Murphy's chicken carcase. Both were ravenous, but Con knew for whom Robbie had brazenly stolen from the larder. As Kevin ate and drank from the water bottle, which had lived through the trenches of Flanders, he gathered strength and composure. Martin had risked his life for him but, as the dawn broke, he had realised his own predicament. Kernahan was no Casemond, as the countryside knew all too well. His rasping voice had risen above the noise of the fire and both men knew that Kevin lay here in pain and danger through his night's work. These were early days and 'the War' was still in its infancy. Irishmen have long tongues, but long memories also. Kevin's gratitude at being hidden here in this dark cavern had been great, but a cold lonely fear had crept over him; and his discovery by a child whom he didn't know had only increased his anxiety. Now here was Con O'Toole, a member of the group, to whom he could pour out his fears. The blanket already made him feel warm and his parched mouth was softened by the cool water.

'Did Martin give you ere an idea for yourself?'

'Ah! shure the poor man beset with his problem and he not back at Ardmore where that bastard would sniff him out and it'd all be up.'

In his simple way, Con was pleased that Robin's find had been Kevin. At least this belonged to last night and did not present yet another problem. It was all part of himself, but he had been more lucky. Also, he had admired the way Kevin, just arrived from Dublin, had spoken up on the bog. God! How long ago that seemed now. Though he admired Kevin, Con revered Martin. Now under fire, he would carry on Martin's work.

'Me lad, lie here and rest. The blood from your leg has stopped. You've had a bite to eat and there will be more. Martin quits at 5.30 and will try to get back here. I'll be with you by 7.30.' Con was thinking of his mother and Ed and their evening tea. 'You're alive and you're safe, thank God!' Con crossed himself and Kevin was impressed. 'Be easy now boy.' Con pulled a packet of Woodbines from his pocket. He looked at the pile of straw, lit one and handed it to Kevin. 'These are hard times,' he tried to sound light-hearted. 'Take a pull on this; it's enough for the both of us.'

The cigarette finished, Con stamped it into the damp floor. 'Thanks, Con.' The voice was weak but contented. As he retraced his steps across the fields, Con thought of that small boy, only eight years old. In adversity, allies come from strange quarters, but now he wished all this didn't have to happen.

The news spreads

Mrs. Murphy warmed her hands before the big black range; she had pulled the damper out fully to let the fire draw. Through the window she could see her faithful admirers, whose home was the stable yard: an assortment of animal life – hens, ducks, several geese and, of course, Master Robbie's billie goat. The morning was glorious. She opened the back door and threw out a handful of oats. Immediately, the yard was filled with noise as the birds fought, flapped and squawked around the corn. Only Bill stood aloof. Corn held no interest for him, but he knew the way to Mrs. Murphy's heart. He ambled towards her and put his head down. The folds of her clean white apron were his target. He butted his head against her generous thigh and then his lip nibbled her empty right hand, but in the pocket sat a sweet biscuit.

Across the yard came young Pat O'Shea – one of Merlin's small army, who between them kept the lawns and gardens in good order. Pat's face was flushed thought Mrs. Murphy, but then he had ridden his bicycle from Rynah.

'Did you hear the news, Ma'am?' Mrs. Murphy was held in respect and even awe by all the Merlin staff. Her blank face showed Pat that she had heard no news and indeed how could she at 7.30 a.m. on a summer's morning.

'Burned to the ground it is. Only the blackened shell is left.'

'And what, young man, is 'burned to a blackened shell' may I enquire?'

'The Rynah barracks, Ma'am, last night and the flames

agin the sky. Shots and all there were, and 'twas said blood and even murder was among it all.'

'Well,' said Mrs. Murphy, shrugging her shoulders in superior fashion, 'I always did say they shouldn't have quit and left them barracks open to the rebels. They should have stayed to keep some order in the countryside before we're all murdered in our beds.' Pat thought that, however sanctimonious the cook's voice sounded, there was a certain relish in it.

Half and hour later Con, unnoticed, slid round the back wall of the old garden and watched a car sweep up to Merlin's marble steps. As Colonel Kernahan jumped out, Con's master came through the doorway.

'Have you heard the news, Alec? A bunch of bloody rebels set fire to our barracks last night. God, what a blaze! They must have used petrol. Mick Cadden, who was walking down the street and saw the fire start, says it began on the top floor. Obviously, all planned in advance. I was on my way home from a duck shoot at Enhalla and got there as the rats were crawling out of the building. Damned hard shooting, but I'm certain I winged one of the bastards. Even though there was a hell of a din, I could swear I heard a scream. I've just stopped there now and God, what a shambles and stink of charred timber! Of course, there's the usual crowd of gormless creatures standing gawping around. Soon shut their traps when I arrived; wouldn't trust a damned one of them. Put the whole lot up against a wall if I had my way. Well, I'll be on the road again, old chap, heading for Kahirloch for a conference with the military boys; got to put a stop to this sort of blackguardery.'

As Jim Kernahan started away, he leant out of the car: 'Oh! forgot to tell you. I found a nice patch of blood at the back of the barracks where I fired a couple of shots. No actual body though, of course the rats may have cleaned up. Well, we will see, we will see ....' His words came back on the breeze.

It was the custom of the Master of Ardmore to inspect his staff and the work in hand for each morning. Colonel Kernahan had served in India. The native troops were stupid and, therefore, deceitful; but he, Jim Kernahan, knew how to handle them. Shout at the bastards to make them understand – God, were all Indians deaf? After years abroad, he returned to take over the family estate. His father had died some years before, but Jim could not immediately leave the army. Ardmore had, during those intervening years, slid back into a state easy to observe in the Ireland of many centuries. The rich and fertile soil produces a growth that gets quickly out of hand and Ardmore's well kept lawns, trimmed hedges and carefully planted shrubberies were hardly recognisable when he and Etta had returned from the gay social life of Quetta. His right hand in those days had been John McCarthy; born and raised at Ardmore he knew no other life but now he was no more – consumption had carried him off ahead of his time. Today, Ardmore was left in the care of John McCarthy's son, Martin and a bunch of local paddies. What was it about Martin that the Colonel could not understand? God knows, he had tried. At first he had thought Martin young and callow, but in recent months, and particularly since the Raheen Regatta, Martin had been – well different. He was always polite and respectful, but there was something which the Indians had never displayed. Was it cynicism or worse a spirit of muted rebellion?

Jim Kernahan had not served in the Army for nothing. He was well known in India for his spartan discipline, and this Irish peasant, this whipper-snapper, was not going to challenge his authority. Earlier that week, he had taken fifteen minutes to tell young McCarthy what he thought of his manner. But it had been difficult. His Indian servants had looked shyly down at the floor when he berated them. Martin had said not a word, but stared him straight in the eyes, and worse still, his white teeth, which Etta often referred to, had gleamed through a well-shaped mouth, twisted – yes, into a slight smile.

It had been his intention to find criticism of Martin's work this very morning, for Jim had convinced himself that his condescending attitude would spread through the other outdoor staff. Now all had changed. The shameless burning of Rynah Police Barracks had violated not only his years of authority but still worse his faith in the established order of his native land. As owner of Ardmore Castle, he was squire of Rynah and this was a personal insult to him as the present representative of his long line. Martin could wait. Jim was impatient to share his experiences of discipline with the local Military, securely stationed at Kahirloch. Their lorries had arrived at the burning barracks in answer to his telephone call from the Rynah post office. It had been closed since 5.30 p.m., but Mrs. Delaney had been at her door watching the 'goings on'. Of course, he had stopped at Merlin to have a word with his old friend; but Alec Casemond, who was such an easy-going chap, couldn't care less. Of course he had only seen war service and really preferred his yachting – never had a tough army training in his life.

Kahirloch in Jim's youth was a sleepy village, but at least it boasted a railway station, which Rynah did not. Since the evacuation of the isolated Rynah Police Barracks, its Military barracks had risen in stature, but first he had an appointment with the Military command. Barbed wire, rusting already in the damp climate, surrounded it in generous layers. The Union Jack, God bless it, flew overhead. Jim Kernahan was well known and he halted for no sentry. The commanding officer's door had never been knocked on by this product of Sandhurst and Quetta. Inside, the large desk was empty, an army clerk sat at a small one in the corner.

'Mornin', where's the Captain?' Grey slacks and an old worn sports jacket with two salmon flies protruding from the lapel did not disguise the voice of authority. The clerk shot from the office and half a minute later Jim Kernahan heard the voice of Captain Henry Clarke echoing down the corridor.

'Most decent of you Colonel to alert us last night. Our report for Dublin Castle is now complete. Probably you would like to read it.'

Jim read the typed statement: 'At 10.26 p.m., information was received by telephone that the evacuated barracks at Rynah was ablaze, the fire having been started by rebel elements. A contingent was immediately despatched in four military lorries. On arrival, the fire was seen to be well advanced. All floors were alight. The Rynah fire wagon was on the spot and was endeavouring to extract water from barracks well. The very limited supply of water available had little effect. A crowd of locals had gathered near the blazing building and order was being maintained by Colonel James Kernahan, owner of neighbouring Castle of Ardmore. The Colonel gave information that he had fired shots at obvious incendiarists and claimed that at least one fugitive from the burning building had been wounded. An extensive search, helped by the headlamps of the lorries, did not reveal a body, but blood was found at the rear of the building. A house to house search continued through the night and early dawn, but so far has revealed nothing. The inhabitants were unanimous in proclaiming their innocence and ignorance as to the causes of the fire. Inquiries are continuing with the firm intention of locating and punishing the guilty parties. Signed: Henry Clarke, Captain, D.S.O.'

Jim Kernahan handed back the despatch: 'Thanks Clarke.

It's shocking business. Can't make up my mind whether it's a local job or engineered from outside. Honest to God, I find it hard to believe that Rynah possesses a chap with the brains to organise such a thing. They're a numb-skulled bunch of morons, you know.'

Captain Clarke had not long been stationed at Kahirloch, but even in the short time he had learned not to get entangled with this Colonel whose career had been spent far from the shores of Ireland. Even though he himself had never been to the East, he felt sure that the minds of the ordinary Irishman held recesses deeper than those of most Indians.

'Quite so, Colonel. Indeed I'm sure you are right. These countrymen of yours' – Captain Clarke was a Yorkshireman – 'are so devilishly clanny. Although they look and protest innocence, it's obvious that many back doors and hay-lofts are ajar to fellas 'on the run'. Ah well! I had news yesterday, just before this wretched business. News which may be well fitted to this present prank. You know, no doubt, that Lloyd George has had a great response to his call for 'volunteers'. Dublin is aflood with them and the Castle is parcelling them out to various parts of the country. Because of the importance of the bridge here at Kahirloch, they have decided to give us a healthy bunch of these new chaps – all fresh from good old Blighty.'

Jim was both surprised and relieved at this news. Although he liked Henry Clarke well enough as a man, he could not help feeling that he was tolerant to a pitch of weakness. Furthermore, he knew that these new men had not been too carefully selected, particularly as far as their sensitivity or manners were concerned. He hoped that they would strike terror in the hearts of the locals, a terror which the patient and comfort-loving soldiers under Clarke's command had not in his opinion attempted to do.

'It's a damned shame you didn't pick up that fella I winged last night. If I'd got him, I would have stood him against a wall and given him sixty seconds to tell all he knew and the names of his pals. Maybe I can scare my headman into talking. He's lived in Rynah all his life.' Jim was boasting, for he knew he had little hope of getting Martin to talk. Now his father – that would have been different.

As the day wore on, Martin thanked God for the Colonel's absence. Strong though he was, he felt increasingly tired. The strain of last night lay heavy upon him. It had been the culmination of days of planning, and with their first real action came the realisation of what it meant to be leader of his group. Gone were the days of dreaming. Blood had been drawn, unfortunately on his side; but they had lit a beacon to show their refusal to accommodate the foreign thugs which Dublin had reported to be arriving in shoals.

He was quite aware of the tension between himself and his employer, and he became increasingly worried by it. Could the Colonel suspect? It was of paramount importance that he should not, for, as the self-appointed leader of local authority, he and Martin were now in direct and deadly conflict. In answer to the arrival of the Black and Tans, I.R.A. Headquarters in Dublin could only increase these acts of sabotage and here in Rynah and for many miles around he, Martin, would be the organiser and leader. The Colonel had the Military in his pocket and at any moment he need only hint the name of a suspect for immediate investigation. Already in many parts of the country men were on the run.

Now Martin was thinking of Kevin. If he were apprehended by the Security Forces, he would scarcely be able to explain the wounded leg. Luckily, he had been away from

Rynah for some time and had only just returned from Dublin with their instructions. Even his mother did not know that her son was back in the district. This was of great luck, for the poor woman could easily have broken down under gruff cross-questioning.

The cavern in Firgrove Wood was as safe a place as Martin could think of to hide Kevin until the hunt died down, but the problem of taking care of his needs was acute. Happily the most obvious had been solved already. As the I.R.A. cells formed themselves they were obliged to be alert to the possibility of the need of urgent medical care. A man could be maimed by the enemy or seriously wound himself in carrying out his mission or trying to escape from it.

Fortunately, Ireland had long been proud of the worldwide reputation she held for her medical teaching. It was generally thought that Merrion Square in Dublin housed the world's best doctors and specialists. Even though the countryside of Ireland with its straggling villages was remote from that elegant Georgian square, there was, nevertheless, a generous coverage of medical men throughout the land. The profession itself was conservative and had studied under the auspices of the Crown. Nevertheless, the worsening of the national situation, the broken promises uttered in the thicket of a world war and the immeasurable roots of the tree of freedom, all combined to flow as a spring tide across the conscience of many otherwise conventional citizens.

A doctor's mission is to preserve life, be the body what it will, and so it was that Dr. Lyster, that jovial old character, friend of the gentry, and neighbour of Merlin, had found himself challenged by Martin to perform his professional duties. Martin had waited at the door while the bell which he had pulled lustily echoed down the long stone passage. Cap in hand, he had rehearsed his opening lines:

''Tis a lad from Roscommon that's damaged his leg, Sir. After a bit of game, Sir – poachin' you might say.'

'Dear, dear, a leg – so important to us all and in these country districts too,' Dr. Lyster started, collecting the tools of his trade and dropping them into a black leather case. 'Now, my man, where did you say this er-lad lives?'

Martin braced himself: 'Well, ye see doctor it's like this. I mean to say, the lad is far from home and he hurted his leg up yonder in Firgrove Wood.' Dr. Lyster stopped still, a stethoscope in his hand. Martin felt the burning gaze upon him. An age passed and then the instrument was dropped into the case and the lid snapped tight.

'Well, man. What are we waiting for?' The doctor's voice was petulant. 'In my profession we don't leave damaged legs to take care of themselves. Lead on man, lead on!'

The cavern in Firgrove Wood was so near to the Doctor's front gate that Martin felt embarrassed. The good doctor, however, showed no surprise.

'A moment Sir, and I'll see if the lad is sleeping.'

'Indeed, quite so!' The doctor walked away humming a little tune. As Martin entered the dark grotto, he whistled softly the curlew's notes. What else could he do? He dare not mention Kevin's name and he hoped, but was not sure, that the doctor did not know that he was Martin McCarthy of Rynah. In a second he was at Kevin's side. The boy had been sleeping and awoke only at his call. Automatically, Martin's hand went to the youth's shoulder to steady him while he explained the doctor's visit. Instead of the straw, he felt to his amazement a rough blanket.

'Kevin, wake up boy and quick. There's a doctor here to see your leg. What's this over you? Who's been here?' Martin's voice was hard and demanding. The reaction was not what he expected. Instead of a stuttering excuse, Kevin sighed contentedly.

'Ah, Martin! 'Twas a little lad who found me here gitterin' wi' the cold. Sez he, sure that's not good fer ye and I'll fetch ye a blanket and a bite t'eat. Within the hour, didn't he send back Con O'Toole – a horse blanket in one hand and a chicken and water in a bottle and all in t'other one.'

A cough outside reminded both men of the doctor's presence. Martin went to the entrance and led Dr. Lyster to the pile of straw. As his eyes became accustomed to the half light, the doctor set to work on Kevin's leg; professional skill in those days was used to surmounting hazards such as poor lighting or lack of running water.

Half an hour later, he stood with Martin outside the cavern lighting his pipe. 'The leg is not seriously damaged. I have cleaned and dressed the wound and removed some shot. A few days rest should have the lad back on the road. Frequently, I take a walk in this beautiful and peaceful wood. Tomorrow at approximately the same time I shall pass this spot. If the lad needs any help, he shall have it.'

Martin doffed his cap and as he smiled his white teeth gleamed. 'The blessing of God on you Doctor. If we live, you'll never regret this day.'

'Nonsense man,' came a spluttered reply. 'Just my duty. Good morning to you.' The protest did not convince Martin and, as he watched the dapper figure making its way through the ferns, he was grateful that he had had the courage to ring the old rusty door bell.

'But, Martin, the boy followed the dog right in here. I tried to hide in the straw, but they found me. Master Robin of Merlin it was, God bless him. An' didn't he steal a chicken from me own Aunt's larder – Biddy Murphy, the auld besom?'

67

As leader of this whole district, trained in secrecy, what worse fate could have befallen him than this single casualty from their first operation should have been discovered by a child and the son of the Master of Merlin – a gentleman and a former officer in the British Army. Oh God! What ill luck! But even as Martin's official reaction burned within him, his heart warmed to the little lad who had been so friendly at the Raheen Regatta. If only he could keep a secret. But then hadn't he said that Con was his idol and wasn't Con one of them now? He must see Con without delay and have him make as sure as it was possible with any eight-year-old child that he held his tongue.

In the evening, Con kept his promise and, on his way home, took Robin via the cavern. The day's lessons had been a failure and Miss Livingstone, a simple soul, felt sure that Robin's distraction was caused by the coming of summer. She had, however, promised him that if he worked hard on his arithmetic during the afternoon, he could, as he begged, go and look for that bird's nest in Firgrove Wood before his supper. The invalid in the straw couch was warm and grateful. Yes, he had slept during the day and when Robin went off to refill the water bottle from the stream on the outskirts of the wood, Con, who had noticed the leg bandages, heard of Martin's and Dr. Lyster's visit from Kevin.

To both youths, Martin's visit was accepted automatically. He was their leader, but what of the old doctor? How indeed had he reconciled his conscience, nay his allegiance, to allow himself to care for a wounded stranger lying in such suspicious circumstances? The class to which the doctor belonged had, for centuries, adopted the customs of the British who ran the country. Indeed, the great percentage of upper-class families were of British stock – hence the term 'Anglo-Irish' or more cynically 'West Britons'. The present attempt to obtain

Ireland's freedom was conducted, with notable exceptions, by the lower classes. The frequent warnings from Dublin Castle against harbouring or even assisting the rebels could indeed make Dr. Lyster's position delicate. But Martin had brought him to the wood and Martin was their leader. It suited Con and Kevin that times were changing: now an Irishman would look after his fellow countryman even at the risk of breaking foreign laws.

Two days later, Con told Robin that Kevin had gone. Kevin had sent his thanks to Robin. Robin in turn promised to keep Kevin's secret safe.

A flame of a different hue

The Irish Mail, bound from Holyhead, that quaint fingernail of Welsh soil, rattled its journey over the sleeping miles towards London. Meli, alone save for a carriage companion, allowed her mind to float across the last few years of her marriage.

She realised that, originally, the Irish Sea – indeed each of its seventy-four miles – had been a gulf that her love and infatuation for Alec had bridged quite simply. The guns of Flanders were not audible in Tipperary, although a million khakied men had ploughed through muck and torment to the tune of the same name.

The rhythmic click of the carriage wheels beat out the strain once more.

Why then had their life together changed so much? Could the fault be hers? Here on English soil, she could ponder anew. To her, Alec had become so self-contained. A true sportsman, he lived for the interests that dominated every Alec through the centuries.

Yet, enmeshed from birth in the custom of her class, there had come to burn in Meli's heart a flame of a different hue.

On *Christina*, their houseboat, at the regatta she had subconsciously tried to ward off the endless visits of Alec's relatives and friends. The reason why she knew not, but as the wheels clicked on, fleeting visions, thin as gossamer, floated before her closed eyelids. Poor figures bent against the purple sunset: rain beating upon them – she could smell the stale dampness of their sodden clothes mingled with peat smoke.

A brilliant shaft of sunlight, which seared through a leaden sky, revealed a figure, not tall but immensely strong, standing erect in the bow of the frail boat – a rope was in his hands as he waited to meet the *Christina*'s stern.

Suddenly, the clicking of the wheels became confused; the train sped on through a junction. Once more the rhythm came, the sweet rhythm which brought peace and with it the smiling, handsome face of Martin McCarthy. Meli slept.

Almost the end of an era

The summer days passed, helped by Nature's rich cavalcade. All day the birds sang in meadow, wood and hedgerow. In the evenings, cows released after milking sauntered through the yard gates and back to the fields near the wood. As they went mooing contentedly, they swished with their tails the flies following in their wake. Smoke curled peacefully from the tall chimneys of Merlin and, as evening fell, the water birds out on the Shannon tucked themselves to bed in the tall green rushes.

Since the burning of Rynah Barracks over two months previously, much had happened. Meli had returned from England to a troubled Dublin. Scarcely three days had she spent there, but it had been enough to feel the bitter tension that now lurked through the city's streets. Fresh from the Edwardian atmosphere of her home, she longed for the smell of the western bog, away from a city that was glorious to look at, but sick to the depths of its heart.

Alec had fetched her in that miracle, that dernier-cri of automobiles of the early twenties – a Vauxhall 30/98, a true sportsman's car, fast and uncomfortable. The long, badly kept road had even less traffic now than when she and Alec had driven Robin to Dublin in the Ford earlier in the summer. How different it all was after England, the roads excellent and the hedges clipped. Alec braking hard brought her back. They had just rounded a sharp bend and there not a hundred yards ahead was a simple but effective road block. With her husband's impulsive nature, Meli expected him to leap from the car, and with suitable epithets, start pulling down the rough stones and wooden barrier. Her restraining hand on his arm was hardly necessary, for during her absence Alec had heard frequently of these blocks. They were erected by either side but with one very obvious difference. When the Military erected theirs, they remained beside them, guns in hand; whereas when the 'rebels' erected theirs, they were frequently for ambush and therefore, they were mostly found where the hedges grew high and a gate to the neighbouring field was at hand.

This was obviously of the second category. Alec switched off his engine and lit a cigarette. For several minutes the silence was only broken by Meli's calming voice, then from behind the hedge slouched four men, caps pulled down over their foreheads, hand in macintosh pockets. No words passed. They peered into the car, opening Meli's suitcase. Alec turned red. This was not his customary role to sit silently while unknown men searched his wife's luggage. Meli's restraining hand rested on his; it was cool and soft. The tallest of the four men jerked his head towards the barrier. Alec stepped out of the car, walked to the front and swung the handle. In silence, Alec and Meli drove through and on towards Merlin. Not a word had been exchanged.

Meli's present mission tore at her heart. She had returned to get Robin packed for his boarding school in Dublin. This re-opened on 21st September.

The avenue of beeches leading from the Gate Lodge to Merlin were tinged with gold. Mrs. O'Toole had been waiting to greet the car. Meli noticed deeper lines on the woman's face, but the smile was still warm and those eyes were deeper blue than the deepest pockets of the River Shannon.

Robin's voice was ecstatic. He jumped into the car, hugged his mother, jumped out again, only to return followed by Scram, wet and smelly from a bog hole. His tail swished black mud over Meli's coat and motoring veil, an asset without which a lady did not travel in those days, for the roads, mostly unmetalled, were narrow and dusty. High hedges kept dust swirling around and, even under the car, it edged through the floorboards and matted the occupants' clothes and luggage.

Merlin's staff did not wear the conventional uniforms of large English houses, but to Meli, after her hundred mile drive through field and bog, their faces radiated a warmth not tinged by servility. Here were people who loved her, not changed by the angry post-war surge to freedom and confusion that she had seen in England.

Nellie and Phoebe ran down the steps, pink cheeked and twinkle eyed. They respected Meli affectionately, but in addition they knew that she always brought exciting presents when she returned 'from the other side'. Faithful Ed hovered round the bonnet of the car, the reins from the horse's bridle all but there in reality. Con came shyly through the side door from the yard, touched his cap, and started to unstrap the dusty suitcases from the luggage grid. Meli was quick to notice the change in his face: higher colour showed round his sharply cut cheek bones. The beautiful eyes had receded further and his clothes hung loosely on his tall thin body.

As she received their very Irish greetings, her mind suddenly held a picture of the Raheen Regatta. The *Christina* floated there for part of a second and people walked her decks. One, short and dark, flashed his white teeth, and something which only Meli knew, something so small, stirred in her heart.

Ah! There was Mrs. Murphy, red of face and puffing as usual. Her kitchen was far from the front steps and without doubt she had been cooking a welcome home dinner.

High in the sky above Merlin, ostrich-feathered clouds were catching the setting rays of the sun: gold changing to pink, then a deeper red and finally, as twilight gently enveloped the countryside, the stately feathers only slightly distended, showed faintly white once more.

Dinner was indeed a welcome home feast and Robin was allowed to stay up for it. He filled the greater part of the meal with stories of his doings, and Alec and Meli were happy to let him have the stage. Even Miss Livingstone showed interest in all his tales, but she poor dear felt sad. Her sojourn at Merlin was almost at an end: in a week they would all drive back to Dublin and little Robbie would become a schoolboy. Sad is the lot of a nanny or a governess when their wards outgrow the span of care which they can offer.

To ruminate is dangerous

Now it was autumn and the beech leaves had turned red, while wisps of mist swirled gently across the fields lying near the river. The old house lay still and sleeping, waiting for another spring. It was quieter now than in the past when Robin's active mind and shrill voice had contributed so much to its gaiety. Letters from school assured his parents that he was settling down and enjoying his new life, but the void at home created by his absence was sadly noticeable. Alec and Meli had lost the link which had done so much to bridge their different characters. Robbie had always been with them and now that he, as an only child, was absent from their daily life, there seemed less to hold them together.

Alec found his wife receding further into her garden and her books and so he, impatient and footloose, went more often to the golf course and the local county club. Both were centres of gossip. The former included women, whereas the latter was the usual male sanctuary.

'Alec, why are you so irritable nowadays?' Etta Kernahan asked, as they ate their sandwiches just away from the ninth green. Etta was gay, sympathetic and fond of Alec Casemond. She was increasingly bored by her husband's bombastic manner and looked forward to these days on the golf course with Alec.

'God, Etta! I wish I knew. I suppose it's either my fault or Meli's. She seems so remote and cold – so English in fact. Now Robbie's away, there is little going on around Merlin. Meli is either in some part of the garden or hidden under a mountain of books.' He gave a little laugh: 'Suppose I should have married a hot-blooded vixen like you.' He cupped her chin in the palm of his hand.

Until she married, Etta's home had been beyond Galway; but through her youth she had come, at the time of the annual regatta, to visit relatives who lived near Raheen. It had meant as much to her as to the dashing young Alexander Casemond. She had been his crew in so many successful races; and at night they had danced at the various big houses in the neighbourhood. Now here they were years later, both bored with their marriages. Yet it would be wrong to say that Alec was bored; frustrated was a better word. Etta had never warmed to Melissa. There were worlds between them, and Etta, although she would never admit it even to herself, felt inferior to the English girl who had come and swept her Alec off his feet.

'Alec, Meli's trouble is that she is not sympathetic towards us. She only likes the poor people here in Ireland because she can patronise them. Have you never noticed how she prefers their company to people of our class?'

'Oh, Etta,' Alec removed his hand from her chin, 'That's not fair. She is just shy and our people are so different to those she grew up with. They are much more reserved.'

'Reserved be damned! They are stuck up bores.'

It was not the first time – nor would it be the last – that they were to argue over this delicate problem; so silence fell between them. Alec lay back on the soft grass and gazed up at the sky. His mind took easily to reminiscing these days for life so often felt empty. In some ways, although he would never admit it, the shrewd Etta was right; Meli, unaccountably to Alec, did ever more spurn the friendship of their own kind: the recent regatta had proved it abundantly. It was also true that she spent hours, apparently quite happily, in the meanest peasant cottages. As a male, he could not agree that she enjoyed 'patronising' as Etta had said. But it was an odd situation and Alec tried hard to analyse it. By letting the mind wander back through time maybe he could find the reasons for their very different natures.

It was true that while Ireland decayed through the nineteenth century, England's wealth by contrast had increased beyond all known bounds. The Industrial Revolution, followed by the vast extension of the Empire and its fabulous resources, provided large and top heavy upper and middle classes bored in their Victorian security. The younger generation of these families longed for adventure: sons went East to secure posts, well protected by the Union Jack and a host of native servants; daughters, asphyxiated by the heavy blanket of life surrounding them, burned secretly for excitement. So it was that the handsome, dashing and carefree sons of old and mossy estates in Ireland found sweethearts and future wives amongst these Victorian damsels. And exactly in this manner had Meli come to the Dublin Horse Show in 1908 and ultimately found herself Mrs. Alexander Casemond, Mistress of Merlin.

What these young couples had in common was of little importance for, at the time, each provided for the other's needs. Up until 1914, life had been easy; differences of character or interest were hardly felt beneath the layer of sport and entertainment. But with the coming of the Great War, the drain of manpower made increasing gaps in social events and family life. Unlike England, where numerous women's organisations grew up over night, female Ireland drifted along.

The Easter Rising in 1916 was a rude awakening that all was not well. Centuries of automatic recruitment to 'the Flag' were in question. Was this world struggle the personal concern of a poor island dominated by an alien power for almost 700 years? The Rising was ruthlessly crushed in the name of treachery and rebellion, but many of the 100,000 Irishmen, verminous and despondent in mud-filled trenches on the Western Front, searched their hearts and kept their thoughts to themselves.

Meanwhile Meli and her kind spent these years carving out their own lives. Why should they do so in the Irish fashion, of which they had made small study? It was natural that these young and protected matrons should pursue their daily lives as they had learned in the safe surroundings of Victorian houses.

With the war finished, life over most of the world's surface was to be very different. Social unrest displayed itself in wide variety: from blood lust revolution to rumbling discontent amongst the masses. To Ireland the victorious lads returned in their thousands, and to what? Impatiently, the country waited for generous promises given by England's Lloyd George to be fulfilled. Excuses and procrastination were understandably translated as broken promises and bad faith. Ireland, in common with so much of the post-war world, seethed; but with its own problem. Unemployment, hunger and cold were accepted as part of life, but where was that promised independence? Once more the guns boomed and were joined by the rattle of machine gun fire through the silent streets of Dublin. In the country districts, which were all Ireland but for a few cities, little happened at first. Sweet and soothing were the smells of turf and hay after rancid trenches with their rotting corpses. A modest gratuity, coupled with relief from leggings and putties, were enough to keep the country boys happy. Time enough to worry about employment and a weekly wage.

Alec drove to and fro from Merlin to Kahirloch, he shared that relief with the growing mobs of men who propped up the street corners and blocked the entrances to the public houses. Years of continuous danger had made him carefree and this, coupled to his restless nature, combined to make him critical of the sleepy life which now engulfed him. That very danger had been exciting, even exhilarating, and was shared with countless other human beings; but now he was entombed in Merlin, quiet without his son's piping voice. His wife still beautiful but colder, much colder, wandered in a timeless dream, or so it seemed to Alec.

Eila House, his mother's home, was quieter too. Her brood had been scattered by the War and marriage. Emma Casemond reigned over a world of shadows assisted by elderly servants. Alec often turned his steps towards Eila House and would sit on the old flagged terrace drinking Irish whiskey while his mother studied him.

'Mother, what can I do?' he had said to her on one occasion. 'After so long in a man's war, I'm smothered at Merlin. There is nothing to achieve and no danger to make it worth while. It's all so quiet. I can go mad sometimes with the silence of it all.'

'But boy, it's your home and your family; aren't you glad to be back amongst it all again?'

'Mother, I feel guilty that I'm being strangled. Think of life here, at Eila House, with us all shouting at each other and fighting. We 'lived', Mother; Merlin is dead – that is except for Robbie.'

Emma Casemond knew all too well what the trouble was, but unlike most of her sex she resisted the natural temptation to rub salt in her son's wound. How she longed and expected him to marry from his own world; and how troubled she had been when he produced another of these 'English heiresses'. The position had not been made easier when, shortly after the wedding, her new daughter-in-law's family had paid a brief and totally disastrous visit to Eila House. They arrived, through some ill fate, the day before they were expected, or so Emma stoutly maintained. The Grantleys, however, thought otherwise. Nothing had been prepared; for, by Irish standards, all was best done at the last minute. Emma herself was gardening in the wet black soil when they arrived. Her face as well as her hands and boots were bespattered with mud, for the midges had been chronic that day. Two days later on the return from church at Rynah, the wheel of the dog cart had fallen off in pouring rain. Mrs. Grantley's Sunday hat was never seen again. Through all this, the helpless Melissa had registered little. Emma did not forgive her for not having tried, at least, to keep her revoltingly arrogant and sneering family in check. In Ireland you said what you thought and at least intimated disapproval of your parents, if need be. This mealy-mouthed modesty was unknown to the tough breed whence Emma came and she found no sympathy for her daughter-in-law.

Now, here was her son, whom she loved and respected, demented, but still she was too shrewd to hint that she could have told him so. Alec was stubborn and the War had not helped his temper. She could not put the clock back over those vital years, and so why risk his impatience with her also?

Calmly, she spoke of the life of the countryside, of the people who lived and worked the land. In the soft evening light, Alec poured them each a drink. His mother was proud that she had always been able to drink with her men. There was nothing sanctimonious about Emma Casemond. As he left her, sitting there in the dark, calm and serene, to walk back across the fields to Merlin, Alec had taken with him some of that calm serenity?

All this had been long ago. He had settled down, everything had settled down, and now everything was blowing up round him once more – right here in his own homeland. This time he did not get the same thrill, if that it could be called. This was not his fight; the English had done him no harm. Like the Romans in their time, England ruled so much of the world.

For centuries, they had ruled Ireland and it didn't worry Alec or most of his kind. Now buildings were burned, bridges destroyed and murder and death stalked the streets and by-roads. And so after long years of real war, he tried to turn his back on the events going on around him, by playing golf, sailing and fishing – his favourite sports.

Etta's voice brought him back with a bump: 'Alec, where have you been for the last twenty minutes? We have lain here in silence and you have looked so far away. What is it Alec? Have I hurt you?'

He took her chin in his hand once more, a pretty little chin. 'I've been both beyond the horizon and back behind time, me dear, and it's got me nowhere; but it was fun.'

And so they finished their game of golf.

Unwelcome guests

When the school holidays arrived, Alec went to Dublin to fetch Robin home for Christmas and there found the atmosphere even more tense. In the previous October, Terence MacSwiney, the Lord Mayor of Cork, had died of starvation after seventy-four days on hunger strike in an English jail. This had greatly inflamed feelings throughout the country and Ireland now possessed one more 'Martyr'.

In Dublin, shooting at night was commonplace and the roar of an army vehicle in an empty street, followed by the screech of brakes and hammering on a pre-selected door, was no stranger than a meowing of an alley cat. Spying was all the rage; everybody, it seemed, spied on everyone else. The fight for freedom was turning very sour.

The journey to Merlin now took its course according to local hearsay. Frequently, on each journey, Alec would stop at village pubs where he was known to have a drink and ask the news.

'Ah shure, that stretch of the road isn't any good this three week past. Didn't they blow the bridge in pieces a while back. Take the lane past the burned barracks, sir, an' you'll come out by the mill. There's a ford there an' if the rain didn't swell it too much you'll likely get over.'

Or: 'Don't take that road after all, sir; it's stiff with snipers after the Military. Paddy here'll go down with ye past Mick Flattery's farm and bring ye out beyont the school house above on Mardrec Hill.'

And it was thus that Alec made the journey to Dublin and back in the winter of 1920.

Robin's excitement at getting home was ecstatic. He rushed here and there, greeting his mother, the staff, the animals, everything and everybody. To him 'The Troubles' meant nothing more than increased excitement: a blown up bridge, the flames of a burning police barracks lighting the evening sky, all joined in to satisfy his imagination.

Winter, a rare visitor in its extreme, had visited Ireland. Parts of the Shannon offered skating to its neighbours. Robin took Scram for a walk across the white fields and they arrived at the entrance to Firgrove Wood. These last three months had been a lifetime to this small schoolboy, uprooted from an established and secure home life. As he made his way towards the cavern, he wondered had happened to Kevin. Had his leg healed? That first experience of an active role in real drama came back to him as if from another world. Where was the link between his classroom lessons at boarding school and the gripping and poignant drama of the previous summer in which he had played such a vital part? To every boy comes the moment when a guarded secret, or a confidence well held, transports fiction into reality.

In the deep dark section of the wood, Robin came to his cavern. Its entrance looked as he had always known it, but within he found a surprising difference. The cavern was much larger; it housed an old warped table and some crooked wooden stools. Bottles, some broken, were piled in a corner and, where a fire had once burned, lay a heap of charred papers. Always the youthful detective, Robin took some of the less burned pieces to the cavern entrance. Names, once neatly written, showed dimly on the blackened sheets. He read them casually, until he found one which made his heart beat faster: 'Con O'Toole, Rynah repeat' was all he could decipher, but somehow he knew that danger lurked behind these few simple words. Of course, he had greeted Con when he arrived at Merlin. But there had been no chance to talk, too many people were around. Back now in the quiet cavern, he wanted to know more. School had taught him to be independent; indeed he felt old and wise as he stood at the cavern's entrance. He would find an early opportunity to have a heart-to-heart talk with his beloved Con. This came soon afterwards when he found Con cutting firewood in the outer yard. Here they could talk quietly for no one seemed to be around.

'Con, Scram and I have just been to Firgrove Wood,' he watched the other's reaction. Con looked even thinner than when Robin had made the tearful farewell three months earlier. He sighed as he put his hand gently on the boy's shoulder.

'Master Robbie, there's lots that do be going on and it's not for the likes of you. Stay out of Firgrove, there's a good lad. Tell not a soul that you were up there nor what you saw or found.'

Robin blushed: 'You know I kept our secret last time. Where is Kevin?' At nine years old, one is easily hurt and Robin felt wounded that his friend should treat him in such an off-hand manner.

'Dublin,' Con snapped out the word, 'and well. He owes a lot to you laddo and he knows it.'

'And to you,' Robin felt generous. 'I only pinched that old chicken carcase. Ha ha on Mrs. Murphy.'

Ha ha on Mrs. Murphy indeed, her nephew frozen stiff and wounded, lying in a dark cavern, within a mile of her. Families, however close, did not know the role any member might be playing; still less could they have believed that, within twelve months, they would be fighting each other. The horror of civil war was in the shadow of another tomorrow.

85

The mystery of Firgrove and even Con's reticence on the subject quickly became blurred in Robin's mind, for Christmas was around the corner and with it absorbing arrangements for a dance to be held at Merlin on New Year's Eve. By the end of 1920, social life in the countryside had shrunken considerably; but proud Merlin planned to rebel against the surrounding apathy and guests had been invited from far and wide. Already the glasshouses were being emptied and banks of hothouse flowers were placed in the entrance hall and reception rooms. By the thirty-first of December, the petrol gas engine was puffing away and the house at dusk was ablaze with light. Large peat fires burned in every grate and Mrs. Murphy, assisted by a legion of willing but inexperienced girls from the estate cottages, had excelled herself with a stupendous buffet supper. The centrepiece of her triumph was a magnificent turkey and on either side, proudly decorated, sat Pat McIntyre's contributions: a huge ham and a saddle of local beef. The windows and counter of Canty's store looked bare and forlorn after Meli's frequent journeys to the village. At nine o'clock, the first cars started to arrive and Ed with unusual élan flung open their doors and doffed his cap to Merlin's visitors. On the top step stood Alec and Meli, displaying, on this particular night, a radiant happiness.

From behind them came the music of a small but efficient local band. Alec's smoking room had, for the evening, become a well-stocked bar and, as the cars continued to arrive, soon became crammed and noisy. But this was New Year's Eve when the world was celebrating and who knew better than the Irish how to celebrate. By 11.30, the drawing room, now a ballroom and almost cleared of furniture, was a whirling mass. Alec Casemond loved the waltz and this he had made clear to the respectful members of the band. He caught Meli's eye and together they edged their way out into the hall, but it was too crowded. They had promised to meet and have one final check on their plans for midnight, after which the supper room would be opened and the marvels of Mrs. Murphy laid bare before the guests. On the front step, it was quieter, and they stood together happily. During the planning of this dance, which both had looked forward to, they had become closer. Life was good even if Ireland was going through another of her crises.

In the distance, beyond the front gate, a bright light shone and this was soon joined by the roar of motor engines. As they drew nearer, a cold shiver went down the backs of both Meli and Alec. On the lonely roads of Ireland in the winter of 1920, that particular roar meant one thing: the Military, and more likely still the dreaded Black and Tans. As the lorries turned in at the main gate, Mary O'Toole felt the same shiver creep down her spine. This could not bode well for Merlin or its guests, for no one, no true Irishman, invited the Black and Tans inside their doors. To do so might bring disaster in reprisal.

Three large army trucks followed each other down the drive and as they drew up before Merlin's steps, their powerful engines roared, then all was silence. A searchlight from the roof of the leading truck blazed on Alec and Meli still standing in the open doorway. The band was still playing 'Whispering'; but already the news was passing from those near the front door, back through the crowded hall and into the ballroom. Smartly the soldiers jumped down from their truck but, in the blinding whiteness of the searchlight, it was not possible to see what arms they carried or what positions they were taking up. At first there was complete silence; and then a tall soldier wearing a kilt and carrying bagpipes stepped into the beam and proceeded slowly up the steps. At the top, he stood straight in front of Meli and Alec and spoke with a strong Scottish accent.

'Good evening, I think our invitation must have gone astray. My lads would like to join your party; life in these parts can be lonely for strangers.' The light pierced Alec's face, which was white with fury more than fear. Of all Ireland's unwanted visitors through the centuries, these Black and Tans, this 'scum of the English jails' as local publicity had named them, were demanding entry to mix with Merlin's guests. Throughout Alec's long war service in France and Palestine, he would have pulled his revolver from its holster and challenged this impudent intruder. Now here, with women and unarmed men packing his home, he was helpless. He stood in frozen silence.

'It would be a pity to miss midnight,' said the stranger, the corner of his mouth twisted into a smile.

'You will be welcome.' It was Meli's voice which broke the silence.

The soldier looked at his watch: 'We have no time to waste.' He turned and faced the silent trucks: 'Men we are welcome.' He echoed Meli's words, but his voice sounded cynical. Immediately, there was a clatter of feet on the gravelled drive, and up the steps trooped fifty men. The soldier turned to Meli and bowed: 'Thank you. Tell your guests we mean no harm and in return expect none.'

The men lined up behind him and he put the pipe to his lips. Alec and Meli stood aside as the opening notes of Loch Lomond gushed forth from the bagpipes. Into the hall he marched, followed by what Ireland had come to think of as a gang of desperadoes. Merlin's guests, watching their hosts, stood back to make a passageway and through it marched the uninvited men. Into the awed ballroom they went; the couples and the silent band watched in amazement. For a full three minutes they continued their march, well rehearsed and in full self control. When the leader, obviously their commanding officer, finished playing, he took off his bagpipes and laid them by the bandstand.

'Play on,' he said simply and turned towards Meli who come into the room with Alec. He bowed and held out his hand. Instinctively she came towards him. The startled bandleader tapped his bow on his music stand and the strains of 'Destiny' filled the room. The soldiers turned to the women guests, many of whom took their cue from Meli. Those who did not immediately find willing partners, stood in groups quietly by the walls. The band, entirely ignorant of what to do in this extraordinary situation, played on and on. At last, with a sign from the officer, and not from the Master of Merlin, it ceased. Complete silence reigned.

'And now, Madam, I think you have refreshments. My men are hungry and we will no longer disturb the dancing.' Obediently, Meli walked towards the door, through the silent staring hall and into the dining room, followed by the whole troop of soldiers.

'You may all leave now us now and we thank you. We will serve ourselves.' Again he bowed.

As if in a dream, Meli beckoned to the hired waiters, who followed her out of the room. Behind her, she heard the door close. Faces on every side watched her for a lead. Slowly, she walked on till she found Alec at the entrance of the ballroom.

'For God's sake, tell them to play,' she muttered, 'and to go on playing till we tell them to stop.'

Within the hour the dining room was empty. Down the steps walked the unexpected guests. The engines started and, considerably more quietly than at their arrival, the army trucks drove way into the night.

No names had been given and no incident had occurred, save one: Mrs. Murphy's buffet looked as if a pack of wolves had ravaged it. Hardly any food was to be seen and, of the wines, only two bottles remained unopened.

Ambush

Out of Merlin's gate, the trucks turned towards Rynah. Major MacTaggart smiled as he thought of the unexpected visit he had just paid. His men had behaved remarkably well and the buffet was excellent. His only time of anxiety was when they had consumed their wine and still had to make an orderly departure through the crowded and silent hall. Luckily the behaviour on both sides had been exemplary. Ah well, this would teach these stuck up Irish families their manners. He laughed softly to himself as he recalled his opening remark: 'I think our invitation must have gone astray.' That was a good one indeed when not a soul at the dance even knew where he and his men had come from. He on the contrary had heard of Merlin's New Year's Eve festivities well in advance. The Irish talked too much and anyway why should Black and Tans be ostracised when they were here to maintain order in this rebellious land?

What the Major did not know was that from Merlin's Gate Lodge, within minutes of his arrival, a tall thin figure, on a bicycle, had sped back along the Rynah road. Their visit to the dance had lasted barely two hours, but in this time Con had roused Martin and all but one of the members of the Rynah Group. Joe Connery was away from his home.

As Con, breathing hard after his ride, told Martin what was taking place at Merlin, Martin, as area leader, was quick to see the rare opportunity it presented. On the outskirts of the village stood the blackened ruin of the police barracks, with its surrounding walls still standing. These would provide a well protected platform from which to ambush oncoming trucks and, in addition, a thick clump of laurel bushes grew on the opposite side of the narrow road. Martin's group collected their firearms and ammunition, recently concealed in a disused well shaft. Con could give no more information than that 'they were in possession of the big house and only the Lord knew what would happen before the night was out'. Martin would take no chances when such a quarry was at hand. The 'scum' never went long when they were visiting. For a moment, his mind strayed to Mrs. Casemond: in contrast to his fiery nature, she was cold and calm, but then she was 'from the other side'. So were these rats, who were raping his country. Murder was their sport. Would she, could she, approve of their tactics? Sinn Féin's leaflets, profusely distributed and increasingly inflammatory, painted an even blacker picture of horror. While he realised that her kind would be unlikely to have access to the leaflets, he did not wish to believe Mrs. Casemond could sympathise with these perverted jailbirds. Well, she must think what she wished to think, for it would not impede the struggle in which he was involved.

Martin, squatting behind the stone wall, saw in the faint light of a quarter moon a figure creep silently from the bushes and cross the empty road. It was Con.

'Maybe 'tis all a failure, but they came from this direction and there's not a turn off worth the name between here and Merlin.'

Con gave one of his rare, shy and apologetic laughs. 'For shure 'tis deep out of the ground they came and isn't that where they belong anyhow?'

The words were hardly finished before the distant roar of engines pierced the quiet winter's night. Martin's men needed no instructions. Without further word, Con slid back into the laurels. He and three others pulled out from the darkness heavy wooden beams taken from the ruined barracks. Martin's boys lifted lumps of fallen masonry over the wall and set them across the road. Within sixty seconds, they had set an ambush through which no car would try to pass. Back in their positions, they watched the brightening glare in the sky.

'This is it boys,' called Martin. 'Our chance has come. Long live Ireland! Up the I.R.A!' Weapons of death waited on both sides of that little unpaved road, where humble donkeys had carried their loads since the beginning of time.

The first lorry's driver, surprised at what appeared through his windscreen, pulled hard on his hand brake. He had drunk more wine than some of his fellow men. What was this unexpected obstacle in the road? The men behind him in the open lorry lurched forward and continued to sing 'Bonnie Scotland'. Major MacTaggart, satisfied with his night's success, had dozed off. 'What the hell!' He never spoke another word. From both sides of the road a cascade of bullets showered into the leading truck. The major slouched back, a thin stream of blood flowing from his right temple.

From the other two trucks, men jumped to the ground. Those with revolvers in their belts fired to left and right. It was an ambush indeed. Blazing acetylene headlights lit up the foreground, but on either side of the road lay darkness and enmity. As men fired their bullets into that darkness, the first truck slowly pushed aside the hastily erected barrage.

'Back men, let's go!' called a husky voice and in the partial silence that followed only two further shots were fired at the stark ruin of the barracks. From behind the wall came a piercing cry. Martin, knowing victory was his, had stood up to watch the shambles of his enemy slink away in defeat. It was this last bullet which entered his body – another night's work had taken its toll.

Explanations

Robin's school holiday had been short and within a few days of the Merlin dance, he was once more seated beside his father on the road to Dublin.

The whole evening had felt like a dream to him. From the top of the black oak staircase, he had watched the guests arrive. Several of the women wore turban-like creations on their heads, and from these protruded ostrich feathers. Their dresses had fringes of small fur tails, which made them look to him like the oriental pictures in his own books. He too had seen the bright lights of the advancing trucks and had watched the arrival of the Black and Tans, through the banisters. His first meeting with the bagpipes would always be remembered, even though they brought with them an air of tension; and he knew that the visitors had greatly upset both his mother and Mrs. Murphy as far as the dining arrangements were concerned.

Then there had been that further tension and embarrassed silence after he had shot into the smoking room when Colonel Kernahan from Ardmore had arrived at Merlin the morning after the dance. He had overheard them discussing 'the ambush'. Nobody had wanted to tell him about Rynah and his father had asked him to leave the room.

Even Con, formerly a useful and willing source of information, was hopeless. When Robbie pressed him, adding tactlessly that 'they' were talking about it in the smoking room after Robbie had stayed long enough outside the door to ascertain at least the reason for Colonel Kernahan's visit, Con had blanched and said tersely: 'What went on in Rynah is not for the likes of you.' Robbie was cut to the quick; this was not the Con he knew and now, as he sat in the car next to his father, he still was little the wiser and yet he had another long term to go through far away at school and no way of finding out.

Suddenly he had an idea: 'Dad, won't you tell me about Rynah? It's all so mysterious, those strange people arriving with whatever it was making such a noise and drowning our band. Then Mrs. Murphy' – he purposely didn't mention his mother, because he had eavesdropped to hear her reaction – 'being so furious about the supper and now all this Rynah mystery and even Con wouldn't talk about it.'

He knew he shouldn't have said this last bit, but it was too late. They had been driving slowly along the badly surfaced road, shielded from the cold winter day by the canvas hood and tall side curtains.

His father looked sharply at him and brought the car to a halt at the side of the road, switching off the engine. As he lit a cigarette, he said almost distantly: 'Why should you think Con could tell you?'

At nine years old, Robbie was alert for his age. Had he not shared his own great secret of the man in the cavern with Con, he might have fallen into his father's trap; but that event, better than any boy's stories he had read, had taught him from the theft of Mrs. Murphy's chicken the need and value of keeping certain things from his parents.

'Oh, Con's my friend. I tell him everything.' Although he had never heard the word 'nonchalant', Robbie certainly acted his part well.

Alec was forestalled by his son's frank reply. He puffed at his cigarette and thought again: 'Robbie, you are nine now and a schoolboy and probably should know more of what is going on in the country. These are bad days for Ireland, and I fear there are worse to come.'

It was difficult to know how much to tell the boy whose frankness he always admired. 'Ireland wants independence and there are many desperate people who are determined to get it by any means. Promises were made when I was at the War, but they don't seem to be coming through.' He tried to pick his words carefully. 'Those men who came to the dance are called 'Black and Tans' and are sent from England to help the Forces to keep order. They have, in many parts of the country, earned a very bad name from themselves. On their way home from Merlin, the group that visited us were ambushed and their leader, Major MacTaggart shot dead. Now there's hell to pay and they are determined to find and punish the culprits.'

Robbie's mind was thinking fast. Was this why Con had been so unkindly short with him? Oh Lord! Was Con one of them and would they shoot him? Now here he was going to this silly school where 'lights out' in the dormitory took place at 7.30 p.m., when he should have been at Con's side. His mind flashed further back to the wounded man in the cavern, who he had befriended, even borrowing his father's water bottle to take him the drink for which he had begged. It was not difficult to link the stories he had overheard about the burning of the Rynah Police Barracks with that of the wounded man. He longed to tell his father all about it, but there was his solemn promise to Con. If he told his father now, Con might even be sacked or punished for helping him – and he had been Robbie's own find. Fortunately, before he could decide what to do, his father continued:

'These Black and Tans are tough and they mean business. I fear for our people, Robbie. I'm glad that I'm getting you back to school, old boy, where you will be away from it all. I didn't like leaving your mother alone at Merlin, but she refused to come with us. Said it made her feel less sad to say goodbye to you at home than to go all the way to Dublin and have to do it there. Oh well, I'll be back the day after tomorrow ...' An Army convoy rattled by, splashing mud over the Vauxhall. Angrily Alec started to wind up the engine:

'I wish to God they would all go home,' was all he could think of to say in front of his young son.

But it was not the day after tomorrow, nor even the next week that Alec Casemond was to see Merlin again. At the Shelborne Hotel, meeting place of Irish society since the previous century, he ran into his brother Harry from Drumalla, on his way to London.

'Alec, for God's sake, come with me; I dread going alone. Allison, poor girl, is in bed with 'flu; it would make all the difference if you will come along too.'

Alec had just come back from leaving Robin at his school. Even though it was so long ago since he had been deposited in that same hallway, and there had been the War between, he would never forget the soulless feeling he himself had experienced in those far off days. What he needed was a stiff drink; and after three, both he and Harry decided it would be a right good thing if he did accompany his brother to London. Meli would understand he felt sure as he handed the telegram to the Hall Porter.

Craving romance

'Emma Casemond is old and ugly,' Emma said to herself aloud, as she pulled on her straw gardening hat. Without the interest felt by most women, she glanced into the hanging mirror surrounded with chips of mother of pearl. It had been a wedding present from a beau, one she had not chosen. At the back of the frame, held by a clip, was a little poem, which the heartsick suitor had composed. Emma hadn't looked at it for many years, but now her hand plucked the little yellowing envelope from its hiding place. Carefully she removed the lock of blonde hair and read:

> To you o' fairest of them all
> I send this mirror for the wall
> May it show as would I
> What it sees in its own eye
> Through the years it will be true
> In its estimation dear of you
> From its depth you too may find
> The face of him who stays behind

The young man, who had never married, died defending Khartoum, many years later, for Emma had married in 1874.

What she saw in that mirror surprised her. Of course there were crow's feet around her eyes, but how they flashed back at her in the soft light. Her chin was strong and firm, no duplications hanging around below it. Then the mouth – yes, it had hardened through the years, but she had lost her husband

97

and eldest daughter through drowning in front of her eyes and two of her other daughters through fever of one kind or another in the Colonies. Had she not a right to betray a hardness in her ageing face?

Just as she started to turn, her eye caught in the mirror a shadow passing towards the open front door. Before she could turn round, there stood Meli behind her. Caught looking at herself in the mirror Emma, the old mare of the family, felt awkward and trapped. Furthermore, she was still holding the little yellow envelope with the faded blue ribbon hanging from it.

'Does the mirror tell you the truth?' Meli's voice was more tender than Emma had heard it before. 'It's such a pretty one. I've always admired it; do tell me its history.' Meli sat down in a bamboo chair.

That the Mistress of Eila House had never warmed to her daughter-in-law was well known. There had been little hope from the beginning that Alec's bride would fit into the life that made Eila House what it was. Emma was tough. She came from a family who had lived hard also. In the seventies, the established Irish family had little to fear. Their estates were large and local labour was both cheap and plentiful. As farming was Ireland's only industry and most of the country was extremely fertile, food was abundant to those who could pay for it. For second and third sons, the Empire was wide open; and for daughters, there was a constant turnover of young officers serving at the different military depots throughout the country. Sport ruled Ireland and Emma had joined in a wide variety. From childhood, she knew how to sit a horse and cast a trout fly.

On her rare visits to England she felt uncomfortable and ill at ease. Victorian England and Victorian society were frightening things to an Irish girl and Emma had decided in her early youth that they were not for her. She had been taken to visit one of her aunts in London. It was winter with much cold and fog. The streets as she looked from her bedroom window looked empty and unreal. The new gas lights, which she had never seen before, threw long white beams when the fog thinned and made the pavements appear like black marble. Her mother went out a lot with Emma's uncle and aunt and she was left behind, watched over by a flock of anxious servants. Then in the middle of it all, the Prince Consort had caught a cold and died within a few days. With this great blow to the Queen, life had stopped: only black was to be seen and the days that followed became longer and darker. Emma longed to run from all this gloom and be back in Ireland once more, but of course her parents could not leave until the royal funeral was over.

Years later she had stayed with this same aunt, who was by then widowed. Tea parties followed one another in endless procession and at each the conversation was on two points only. First, would the Queen abdicate in favour of the Prince of Wales to halt all this talk of England becoming a Republic? The very idea of such a thing appalled the ladies in their Victorian drawing rooms. The second subject, and much more interesting, was who would the Ripper claim as his next victim. For some years a murderer, obviously a sex maniac and a lunatic, had struck down lone females in dark and dingy streets. He was never found; but the name given to him became legendary and generations of English maidens shivered at it.

No! Emma far preferred her native land where those things just didn't happen. And so, as years passed, she had been fully occupied in bringing up her large brood, and England, as such, had receded from her mind. Then one day, Alec had produced the girl who now sat before her in the bamboo chair. To Emma, she had represented the epitome of England. Pretty indeed with all the niceties of the Edwardian period, but she seemed weak and tepid beside her own daughters. Then had followed the disastrous visit of the Grantleys to Eila House. The wedding in London, which had obliged Emma to pay one of her rare visits, had found her standing before the house in Montague Square thinking back over the fifty years she had known it. Certainly the summer of 1909 provided a gayer spectacle than the winter of 1861. Meli had looked so beautiful in her wedding dress, but even then Emma had wondered what companionship she would give her eldest son. His infatuation had lasted until the outbreak of the War and then the hectic leaves coming infrequently, often without warning, had provided plenty of stimuli for their two so different natures to blend in harmony. But now with the War well over and Alec back over two years, the differences she had sensed and feared were becoming much more evident. Emma's blood ran thick where her sons were concerned – not always so thick for her daughters – but she did realise that the faults such as they appeared were not all on her daughter-in-law's side. Alec was headstrong and selfish, intolerant also, and his years of war had not improved any of these shortcomings.

Yet, the tone of Meli's voice had touched Emma's tough old Irish heart. She drew up another chair and told the girl the mirror's story, briefly but sincerely. In her hand stayed the little yellow envelope. As she talked, Emma felt the warmth flow towards her from the younger woman and even her usually impassive face glowed with interest. Emma was shrewd and lived the problems of her other children's marriages, but in Meli's case she had never really got beneath the surface. The girl had always been so reserved. Was the fact that she was lonely, with Alec in England, and appreciated this contact with her mother-in-law alone responsible for her present manner; or was it helped in some small way by the story that she, Emma Casemond, was now telling? She had indeed wandered off into the background of her former beau: she had recounted various experiences they had had together; she had even spent a few minutes recounting the story, as it came to Ireland, of his death in far off Sudan. She stopped and saw Meli's wrapped look. With a shrug she tossed the little envelope into the girl's lap:

'He even wrote that rubbish, poor boy,' she said as nonchalantly as she could.

Meli read it silently, put the card back in its little envelope and walked to the open door. For some time she stood there and then, without turning round, said softly: 'How wonderful; maybe it was better that way.'

Now Emma knew what she long feared: Meli was a romantic under her calm English exterior. Indeed, as Emma reminded herself, the girl had waited two years and then had married Alec with her family's barely veiled disapproval. Stuck-up snobs that they were, it must have taken pluck to go through with the marriage. Little help and encouragement had she received from her mother-in-law either, poor girl. In his wild mercurial way, she felt sure that her son had given Meli an exciting contrast to her own tidy and self-restrained nature, but then had come the war with the infrequent stabs of happiness and pain. No brothers for little Robin appeared and now here was this odd foreign girl lonely for what Alec either would or could not give her. Emma was human and she knew that this was the reason Meli had uttered those telling few words.

'You were sweet to tell me your story,' Meli said, as she turned. Emma could see that she had tears in her eyes. Meli kissed her mother-in-law on the forehead. 'Thank you again dear. I'll be off back to Merlin.'

Emma watched as she walked away towards the stile and thought: 'Yes, the girl craves romance and affection and she isn't getting either.' It was a dangerous position and one about which she must speak with Alec in the very near future.

Danger knocks

Wandering back across the fields that separated the two estates, Meli was still thinking of the sad little poem written long before she was born. It was very stupid of her to have made that dramatic statement and she was surprised that Emma had not challenged her remark. In fact her mother-in-law had just sat there in silence. Was she still moved by the poem, or had she too softened as she talked in the evening light?

For her part, Meli had started her life in Ireland by being very scared and self-conscious in the presence of her mother-in-law. This had on a number of occasions grown into a concealed dislike. Mrs. Casemond had, in Meli's opinion, a cruel humour and a hard tongue. She had taken every opportunity to show Meli up as a fool and an English ninny. When Robin was born, she had of course been pleased that the Casemond clan had a future heir; but, as far as sympathy for Meli's health, she had shown none of it, critical only of her rather long accouchement. Emma had ground her babies out like piglets.

In the first years of their marriage, everything had to be for Alec. His hobbies were the only thing that counted. The fact that Alec hardly ever read a book meant that books were a quite unnecessary adjunct to the house and, as Meli's collection grew, so also did her mother-in-law's scathing reactions. But the War had changed all that. She spent long days and weeks alternating between the garden, the nursery and her beloved books. In Merlin, she had made one of the rooms into a library and worthy Willie McGrath, lame and therefore no use for military service, had done a fine job on the shelving. Willie was more than a handy carpenter, being able to patch and mend the many things that go wrong both inside and outside a rambling old house. He had served his time with a good cabinet maker in his youth and this, in Meli's sanctuary as she called it, was displayed to advantage.

As Meli made her way through the daisies that studded the long grass, she too, encouraged by her mother-in-law's reminiscences, allowed her mind to wander back over the years. How passionately she had wanted Alec. She well remembered those nights in New Zealand when she thought the two years would never pass. How she had argued with her mother at first, in defence of her Irish Casanova. Through her mind rang clearly the strains of the Destiny waltz; then Alec's unexpected return from the front in Mrs. Lyster's pony trap, his shaven head putting her off at first; their passionate sex during that brief leave, different from what she had known with him on earlier occasions. Meli knew what she did about sex from Alec only: there had been no one else.

Her path led over a bridge and through a water garden, now overgrown and therefore slightly mysterious. The moon would soon be up and so Meli decided to sit a while on an old rustic seat and wait for it to happen. Really, it was ridiculously warm for January; but this, owing to the Gulf Stream, could happen in Merlin's part of Ireland.

Not far from the water garden stood the old potting shed, one of Robin's favourite haunts. As Meli sat, not wanting to lose her train of thought, she could hear the sounds of the night approach. The animal world was putting itself to sleep. A waterhen clucked nearby and two blackbirds held an excited conversation. A little wren fussed from bush to bush and her impatient twittering brought to Meli's mind the colourful story of the Boyne, and the reason why a whole day, 26th December, was given up to the stoning of these poor birds by the youths of Ireland. Officially known as St. Stephen's Day, 26th December was also known as 'Wren boys' day'. In 1690, William of Orange and his troops massed near Drogheda, some 30 miles north of Dublin. While they slept before one of the bitterest battles in Irish history, the Irish surrounded their camp during the dark winter's night. The ambush which would take place at first light would, according to military historians, have annihilated the British troops. Alas for the Irish, the enemy's drummer boy had eaten his supper of bread and cheese using the drum as a table. The early bird, as an ornithologist knows, is the wren. And so, as the drummer slept and the Irish waited, a gentle tapping was heard. One by one, the tasty crumbs were picked up by that busy little beak. With each peck came another tap. At first the drummer only shifted his position; but, as the tapping continued, the boy began to wake from his cold hard sleep. Rubbing his eyes in the grey dawn, he could at first not believe what he saw. On all sides, shadowy figures in their thousands were creeping towards the camp. The frightened lad jumped to his feet and beat his drum as he had never done before. The camp awoke only just in time to see what he had seen. The Irish did not withdraw, but came on into the now awakened camp. The slaughter that early morning was very great and to this day the River Boyne sighs on windy nights for her lost sons; and the little wren's successors are hunted and killed for her innocent folly.

The moon crept up through the trees and the day birds became silent. From quite near came the call of a curlew. It was soft and Meli, who was always prepared for it on the alternative path from Eila House which went by the river, was greatly surprised to hear the call here in the water garden far from the river bank. Instead of starting to walk to the house, she waited, hoping to hear the call again, but all was silent. She must remember to tell Alec of this unusual experience. The path led past the potting shed and on through the walled garden. As she drew near to the shed, Meli heard a slight noise and the crackle of twigs, as if something or someone was moving.

She drew behind a clump of bushes and waited. The door of the shed was not far off and she could see it clearly in the light of the half moon. A figure appeared in front of it and stood still; from it came the short sharp cough that she knew was Con's. What was he doing here at this hour? He whistled the curlew's call and waited. Slowly and with obvious care two figures appeared carrying what appeared to be a stretcher. It was not empty and what lay upon it was heavy. Fascinated, Meli stood and watched this extraordinary scene taking place in her own garden. The moon threw its ethereal light upon that stretcher and Meli felt a shiver run down her back. The half-moon came suddenly from behind a cloud revealing the body of a man being slowly carried into her potting shed.

During her years in Ireland, Meli had never really felt afraid. Alone during the War except for Nannie and the servants she had learned to love the isolation of Merlin. What she saw now was different. Shadowy human figures were moving silently about her property. To let this situation pass unchallenged was wrong; yet she was well aware of the alarming and desperate state of affairs in her adopted land. The stretcher and its bearers had disappeared inside the shed, so also had Con. At least he knew her and, as far as she could rely on anyone, he respected her and would never harm any Casemond.

Quietly she walked the short distance to the door and stood before it in the pale moonlight. Her mind raced with the pumping of her heart. It was well known that the authorities at Dublin Castle, fortress of British Rule, had ordered a search to be made for all men suffering from bullet wounds. Even hospitals and doctors were under instructions to report all cases brought to their attention. In the city, according to rumour, patients were taken from doctors and nurses dressing their wounds and placed in Military hospitals for questioning. Thus the Volunteers, as the Irish rebels were called, when wounded, were carried to remote places of safety in the hope that they would not be forced into giving away valuable information which would involve their compatriots. From inside came the soft murmur of men's voices. Meli waited, unnoticed.

'Get him a sup of water, Con; 'twill ease his mind.'

Con walked to the door and faced the dark figure standing by it. 'Jesus Christ!'

Meli's voice was soft and gentle. 'Con, can I help you?'

Inside the shed, she heard a shuffling, as in a sleeping hen house suddenly aroused.

Before his coughing started, Con had time to call out: ''Tis the Missus.'

From deep within the shed, she heard a groan and a voice familiar to her muttering: 'God save her: she wouldn't hurt no-one.' The voice was Martin McCarthy's. She had not seen him since those happy days at Raheen. His white teeth flashed into her mind – the swaggering handsome Martin at the regatta. Con recovered from his fit of coughing and Meli put her hand lightly on his thin arm.

'Con come away from this door. I want to talk to you and I am sure I can help whatever you are trying to do.' No question now of being Mistress of Merlin: she was in fact pleading to be part of this extraordinary drama which was taking place on a winter's night in her own garden. Con shivered, not from cold, but from fright. Her grip tightened on his arm. 'It's Martin McCarthy, isn't it?'

'Well Ma'am, the poor devil got hurt and we're tryin' to take care of him.'

To ask how or when would have been hopeless, Meli knew

that. 'Is he badly hurt?' she asked simply.

'Yes Ma'am, his shoulder's broke and he needs a doctor terrible bad.'

'I will go ahead. Bring him to the side door in half an hour. Then you come to the front door where I will be waiting for you. If all is clear, we will bring him into the house.' Meli heard herself talking as if in a dream. She was acting like a lunatic and a criminal. Well she knew that any suspicious act must be immediately reported to the Military. In her case, she knew where her duty lay – as Alec Casemond's wife and an Englishwoman. Before she had time to think how she might retract her offer, Con's damp boney hand was on hers.

'God bless you, Ma'am,' was all he could think of saying.

Could Meli have known, as she walked hurriedly through the walled garden, that not long before her own son had made that same journey and on a similar mission to help a wounded volunteer, it might have helped. Faced, however, with the likely dangers in which her present offer would involve her, she could willingly have turned and run back to Con to tell him that she had changed her mind about using the house itself, but that they could keep Martin in the potting shed for the time being.

Her heart was pounding so hard that she had to stop by the goldfish pool in the centre of the garden. The moon was high now and the servants would be wondering where she was and when to serve her supper. To plan carefully was vital: any wrong move would be fatal. It was stupid to try and delude herself: Martin, however badly wounded, was a wanted man. The countryside was still being combed by the Black and Tans after the Rynah affair, and Jim Kernahan had, as usual, come hot-foot to Merlin on his way to confer with Captain Clarke at Kahirloch. During his vociferous description of the ambush, he mentioned that Martin had not reported for work and therefore was more than likely involved in the bloody affair. As the pounding of her heart grew less, so she could think more clearly. It was now several days since the ambush and it was obvious to Meli, that wherever Martin had been kept, that hiding place had become too dangerous as the hunt for him increased. This realisation sent another shiver down her back. There was probably by now a price on his head and to shield a man in that position was doubly wrong in the eyes of the law.

The night was now cold and quickly she walked to the house. Her plan, as far as she could make it, was complete. The small side door was seldom used and never by the servants. Just inside was a room in which Alec developed his photographic plates. It was his private holy of holies and nobody ever visited there, except on the rarest occasions when he would shout at one of the housemaids for not keeping it clean. They were in fact terrified of the strange bowls of coloured liquids and were certain that they all contained deathly acids. With Alec in England, this room would be the safest possible hiding place and it was convenient to approach through the little used door. It was also at the far end of the house from the kitchen and pantry.

By the time Meli reached the house, she looked calm. Phoebe greeted her: 'Oh Lord, Ma'am, we thought you were lost and it's way past your supper time.'

Meli replied that she had had a pleasant evening with the Mistress at Eila House, and – happy thought – that she had eaten there also. Phoebe looked crestfallen and said that Mrs. Murphy had made her favourite fish pie.

'Ask Mrs. Murphy to forgive me and tell her I would like it for lunch tomorrow. As a matter of fact, I suggest we all have an early night. Just leave everything for this evening, Phoebe, there's a good girl.' Meli was becoming very aware of the time that had already elapsed, and Phoebe looked as if she was screwed to the floor.

'Off you go now, I've got quite a bad headache and talking will make it worse.'

Already Meli was thinking of what she could do with that rather miserable photographic room. The small window was completely painted over in black so that the plates could be developed in safety. The only light in the room at all, if one could even call it so, came from two round holes, each about 8 inches in diameter, cut high in the door. Certainly not a pleasant sickroom, but what Martin needed more than the whole world was a safe hiding place. The awful crime that Meli was committing, and she knew it, was that here in a house like Merlin no one would even think or presume to search out a Sinn Féiner.

Phoebe closed the door of Alec's smoking room, which was near the stairs leading down to the side door. It was a room much used when there were no guests at Merlin, and particularly in the winter, when it was much easier to heat than the other living rooms. Meli was thankful the girl had gone. She had tried to appear calm and the idea of the headache helped. Nellie mercifully was having her day off and Mrs. Murphy never came upstairs except in the mornings, when she discussed the day's meals in Meli's own study.

With luck she would not be disturbed and, taking the lamp, she went quietly down to the side door and slipped the bolt back. As she opened the darkroom door, a mouse ran past her and down the corridor towards the swinging doors of green baize, which led to the kitchen quarters. Inside, the room was dark and untidy. Quickly she tried to put together the mass of photographic equipment – God knows what reason she would give Alec for upsetting his private den. The room was small, but there was room for a bed – but what bed? Why had she not thought of all these things before she had said so foolhardily that they should bring him to the big house.

The guest rooms she dare not disturb, for the maids had instructions to open and close windows and dust frequently. Ah, she remembered Alec had brought back in his army kit a collapsible bed and this was stored, as far as she could remember, in Ed's workshop. Well that would be for Con to attend to.

Time was passing. She did what she could to the miserable little room and went back to the front hall where Con had been told to come. The night was very quiet and she could hear Mrs. Murphy cursing Scram and calling him a miserable thief 'after takin' a fine ham bone from off the kitchen table'. Phoebe's chuckles followed. Thank God the dog was with them shut in the kitchen. Luckily, he loved only two things in his life: Robin and Mrs. Murphy's kitchen, which permanently had a nice hot range and where there was always the good chance that scraps would be thrown to him. Standing at the open front door, Meli felt in a dream. Only those few days ago, she had stood here next to her husband watching the arrival of Major MacTaggart and his men. Now she was awaiting a wounded peasant, probably his murderer, up these same steps.

The gentle rattling of the gravel on the big sweep below announced Con's arrival. He came quickly up the steps, cap in hand, and at the top he touched his forelock and stood silently in front of Meli. The situation she had created probably had no equal in Ireland's long and bitter history. By the difference of their class, nationality, even religion, let alone the fact Con being an estate servant and she the Mistress of Merlin, any of these could and should have prevented the dangerous course she was about to take. In that long moment of silence while they stared at each other, she knew she still had the ace in her hand. Once she gave it away, she would be irrecoverably committed. In the moon's wan light, Con looked so pathetic, his eyes were enormous and his high cheek bones stood out garishly.

'He's terrible sick, Ma'am, and near froze to death with the cold.'

On those simple words from the gaunt youth, Meli took her decision and in so doing turned over a great page in her calm, almost serene life.

'Go to the workshop and get the Master's camp bed: it's with the other kit which he brought back from the War.'

'An' wouldn't I go to hell and back for it, Ma'am, but Ed keeps the shop locked and he has the keys on him.'

Here was the first setback to her hastily made plan. She stepped back into the hall with Con following respectfully, for he only ever entered the house to carry in the heavy baskets of peat for the fires.

Meli told him of her plan for the use of the photographic room and, as she suspected, Con didn't even know of its existence. When she spoke of its shortcomings, Con smiled: 'The bottom of a drain would be welcome, Ma'am, and better than where he has been.' Here their paths parted; for on no account could Meli even ask where or why, even though she was risking all in return. Such was the code of the day.

The grandfather clock in the hall chimed nine. How the time had gone since she had kissed her mother-in-law farewell and started her fateful walk across the fields. To Meli came another of the inspirations she was to have before this drama was concluded.

'Get your bicycle and go quickly to the Gate Lodge. Tell Ed that I urgently want ... a ... er ...' Meli faltered. What could she want from a workshop at nine o'clock on a winter's night?

'A spanner to fix the leak,' said Con simply. As their eyes met, they both smiled. Now they were partners, equals, fellow criminals, working rightly or wrongly for the humane cause – the saving of a life.

Sanctuary is sought

The moon was high as Con bicycled down the Merlin drive, thinking in a dazed way of the position Martin's wounding had put them in. Here was the Mistress about to play a vital role 'on the wrong side of the fence'. Ireland, in the time of the troubles, was still a two-class society with the exception of a small middle class in the towns. The Gate Lodge was dark, which meant that Ed was either already in bed or out visiting, while his mother, delicate and frail, was always early to bed in her small front room. He opened the back door quietly and stepped inside.

There before the dying fire on an old wooden stool sat Ed. Without moving, he said softly, so as not to have his mother hear: ''Tis a lot of wandering that you're at these days, man, and on winters' nights too with that chest of yours.'

He was many years older than Con and had acted like a father to the whole family. Kind, straight-laced Ed, where indeed might his loyalties be lying the way things were turning out, particularly here at Merlin.

'That bloody tank's leaking again and I need a spanner from the workshop.'

As Ed drew the keys from his pocket he spoke again. 'The Military were here this two hours back; they are still ferreting on the Rynah job. It seems them Black and Tans didn't much like their commanding officer being removed from them so suddenly.' Ed was seldom cynical – his younger brother was caught off guard.

'Them dirty bastards,' he blurted out, 'the whole stinking pack …'

Ed turned sharply. 'Careful man, or you'll waken mother.' He could just see Con's face; it was flushed and his eyes stared out in explosive rage.

'Careful man,' he added coldly, 'or you'll waken more than mother. Stay around the big house for the next while. 'Twas you they were asking about. I said you were often late back from the big house, with the hot house fire giving you all that trouble and frost in the air. It seems someone took the news to Rynah that Merlin had uninvited guests; and, to cap it all, that auld devil Kernahan from Ardmore goes tearing in and out to the military every five minutes and now he tells that Martin McCarthy's missing. I'd rather work for the Master fifty times than for that loud-mouthed old weasel.'

Con had stopped listening at the mention of Martin's name. The hunt really was on and here was Ed, either innocently or otherwise, warning him whilst he, Con, was going straight back to help the Mistress of Merlin shield and nurse a wanted man. Families divided in any country and for any reason are always tragic and much worse was to follow before the last pages of Ireland's long struggle could be concluded. In fact, Con would be relieved to talk frankly to his brother, but long years of treating him almost as a father, his oath of secrecy to his group, and now in addition Mrs. Casemond's secret and the danger for Martin's life, all these served as an impenetrable wall between them.

'You look tired, Con. I'll slip down and fix the tank for you.'

Again Con's heart missed a beat. Almost gruffly, he cut his brother short, for he was about to say more.

'Give me the keys and stay by your fire dreaming.'

He took the keys roughly from Ed's hand and walked to the door.

'There's three of us here, Con, to suffer if anything goes wrong; and it is you the Military want to interview. All I got for you was a bit of time to think. They'll be back. The Black and Tans have threatened to baste Rynah if the culprits aren't found and handed over.'

'Handed over' could mean anything. The Tanners already had a bad name for punishment and reprisal. Only the Military stood between them and Rynah.

Con was a simple youth and, though he appreciated the dangerous position he and others were now in, all he could concentrate on was Martin and the Mistress. Hours had gone by since they had moved him in the dark from Firgrove to the potting shed, and more time had elapsed since the Mistress had discovered him. His only thought, as he mounted his bicycle, was to get Martin safely into Merlin and by tomorrow he'd have his own alibi for that fateful ride to Rynah on New Year's Eve.

Robin had given him a small electric torch for a Christmas present. He collected it from the garage, opened the door of the workshop with Ed's keys and made his way to the disused army equipment. There was the bag containing the camp bed, smelling damp and musty. Martin was a lucky man. Since the law forbidding the harbouring of wanted men had been published, many a casualty had died from exposure in the cold winter's nights.

The house was quiet when Con walked to the front door. Meli was still standing on the top step and she looked, Con thought, very beautiful in the pale winter moonlight. Together they went down to the little photographic room: it was warm after the chill out doors. The camp bed just fitted in, with room for a chair. Meli had cleared part of the shelving and this could serve as a table. Only the blackened window looked grim, but, if the weather stayed mild, the top could be left down a bit to enable some daylight to enter and still not attract attention.

When all was ready, Con opened the side door and walked to where he had left Kevin in charge of the roughly made stretcher, concealed behind a bay bush, rich in thick green leaves all the year round. Both men were smoking, something Con was not allowed to do, and briefly he told them what he had been doing. He would not now seek Martin's advice on his alibi, but would ask the Mistress if he could see him in the morning. Gently, Con and Kevin carried the stretcher through the side door of Merlin and set it down at the feet of Melissa Casemond, whose countrymen were now searching for the figure that lay upon it.

The soft light cast by the oil lamp shone down on Martin McCarthy, as he lay helpless looking up at his new hostess: 'We meet again, Ma'am, and I'm sorry to put you to such trouble.'

There still were those fine white teeth and, yes, there too was that smile, not flashing now, but still giving the handsome face its character and rough charm. The youth, Kevin, Meli did not know, but Con had assured her briefly upstairs that he too had had a 'spot of trouble'. Regarding his reliability, Con did not wish to give reasons, but could assure Meli, and he crossed himself to implement his statement, that Kevin's discretion was beyond doubt. Meli gratefully accepted his assurance and, furthermore, she realised that Con could not have carried Martin from wherever they had come alone.

'Con, while you have the key to the workshop, you had better go and get the Master's army cooking kit too. I have all the medical equipment and also plenty of tinned food, but we will need to heat water and I cannot always rely on taking it from the kitchen without causing suspicion.'

If only one of the empty-headed maids, Phoebe and Nellie, could be included in their group, how easy life would be; but naturally that was impossible, unthinkable, when she already had her entire reputation staked on the loyalty of this youth, Kevin.

Her smile, not often seen these days, was adequate answer to Martin's simple words. The less said the better under the circumstances in which these three offenders to the present law were met. Kevin was told, by Con, to wait outside and to make them aware if anyone was approaching. Although at this time of night it was highly unlikely, nevertheless it gave opportunity for Con, Meli and Martin to talk together. Martin's shoulder had received the stray bullet, released in self defence by the ambushed soldiers returning from Merlin, and Meli learned with amazement that Dr. Lyster, that paragon of correctness, had already given him professional assistance. Indeed, his wound had been well dressed, and although he was still in considerable pain, there was little for Meli to do.

With his right hand, Martin produced from the stretcher a small carton. 'Pain killers, Ma'am. If you have a sup of water, I'll take one now and be no more trouble to the pair of you.'

She fetched blankets from underneath the guest room counterpanes and a pillow from Robin's bed. Everything was such a gamble, but at least she could hope that, by being careful, the absence of various needed items would not be noticed by the maids. Martin badly needed sleep and shortly after he had taken his sedative, Meli and Con left him. As she closed the door and turned to look back, there once more was the smile. It spoke all that was necessary of gratitude.

At Meli's request, Con spoke to Kevin on the vital matter of his silence under cross-examination. Wisely Con stressed the danger to Martin as their leader, rather than the delicacy of Mrs. Casemond's position, but Kevin was shrewd and he had received training at headquarters in Dublin. Beside him, Con was a simple country youth. With well-chosen words, he gave his reassurance that no man would ever learn anything of what they had done on this clear January night. Con also told him of Ed's warning. His alibi for New Year's Eve was also urgent. As he walked back through the crisp moonlit fields to collect his bicycle, the youth from Rynah, only eighteen years old, who had now played his part on these three vital occasions, had reason to ponder on this evening's work. To him also, the wounded Martin, now 'on the run', seemed oddly placed in a house such as Merlin. A fine lady that Mrs. Casemond.

An engaging smile

The next morning brought grey skies and rain, soft gentle rain, but when Meli arrived at the small room near the side door, she found her patient in considerable pain. Damp is never good for wounds and poor Martin groaned when she opened the door. Meli felt his brow and found to her relief that it was cool. What could she do to make him comfortable? She and Con had talked late into the night, and had agreed that he would take care of their patient in the ways which she could not. The gravel sweep and paths around the house needed hoeing and this, spread over several days, would give Con an excuse to be constantly near at hand.

At ten o'clock, Dr. Lyster drove his pony and trap over a section of Con's newly raked gravel sweep. Con touched his cap and put down his hoe. Promptly they walked round to the side door and Meli, who had suffered under a French governess for a short period of her youth, smiled from the smoking room window and muttered aloud: '*Quelle delicatesse.*'

Without her presence Martin's wound was dressed and on the instruction of the good Doctor, Con washed the patient. No more than twenty minutes later, Meli found herself chatting to the doctor on Merlin's front step. Indeed she was glad to know that his wife's asthma was better and also his daughter Mary had gone to Dublin as an assistant Librarian. Martin's name was never mentioned and Meli marvelled at the ability of this sincere country doctor to pursue his vocation, unhindered either by politics or military edicts.

The day passed without any of the dreaded events taking

place that she had foreseen during those sleepless hours after Con had left her. In the evening, she took the lamp from the smoking room and went quietly down the stairs. Part of Martin's penance for being a 'guest' of Merlin was that a light in his sick room was out of the question. Con had taken care of his needs and now he lay quiet and comfortable in this sanctuary.

His smile at her entry had much of the old charm. Surprisingly, since this was their first time to be alone, he did not endeavour to apologise for his present position or that which he placed Meli.

''Tis mighty good of you Ma'am to be doing this for me. Won't you sit a while and give me a bit of company?'

Meli's instinctive reaction to this invitation was to make her visit no more than momentary and then hastily retreat. After all, what was Martin McCarthy to her? He was a local lad and a wanted one at that; furthermore he was not even one of the estate employees, such as Ed or Con. He was Con's responsibility, presumably shared with the other youth, Kevin, and heaven only knew who or what else was involved.

'No, really, I only just looked in to see you were alright and I've got a lot of things to attend to.' Her voice was formal and cold but, instead of it having the effect she intended, it brought forth the most engaging of all the smiles she had seen on that handsome face.

As she looked down at him lying on the white pillow something happened within her, something uncomfortable yet thrilling. It was as if a wave swept from her scalp down, down through her stomach and on through her thighs. She felt her knees weakening.

Martin was watching her intently as if he could see her discomfort. She hated her present weakness and him for insolently observing it. Meli dragged her eyes away from his and turned to leave. Now, she knew why it had not been repellent or horrifying to her to invite Con to bring his wounded charge into her home. At the Raheen Regatta presumably something about Martin had moved her, certainly something invisible but significant. Without speaking, she left the little room of which she had never in her years at Merlin had the smallest interest.

Fresh air was what she needed to shake off the odd feeling she had just experienced. Opening the side door, Meli stepped out into the dull winter's day and there, within a few yards of her, stood her mother-in-law, walking stick in hand. For some time now, Emma Casemond had suffered from arthritis and so made use of this door in preference to the more difficult approach up the main steps.

'How pale you look, child; are you unwell?' The older woman scrutinized her daughter-in-law. Not much evaded those shrewd old eyes. Emma proceeded firmly towards the door. Weakly Meli took her arm and endeavoured to halt her progress.

'Oh, it's nothing. I've had a miserable headache all day, probably spending too much time in the library. What I need is some fresh air.' Her grip tightened on the thin arm. 'Do come with me. I want to smell the jasmine in the greenhouse.' Meli had remembered, with horror, that she had in her confusion left Martin's door ajar.

Obediently, Emma allowed herself to be led away from the disaster which would have taken place, had she arrived one half minute earlier. As they crossed the lawn leading to the main garden, Con appeared carrying a basket. He saluted both women and quickly turned in the direction of the back door, which led to the kitchen. Another dangerous moment had passed: for Meli knew that in that basket were supplies for Martin.

Emma Casemond was full of news and wanted to share it with her daughter-in-law. Living alone, these days at Eila House were dull after so many years in which her off-spring had come and gone in steady procession.

'Imagine the impertinence,' Emma snorted, 'a group of those miserable Black and Tans driving up without a by-your-leave and actually cross-examining me about the Rynah ambush. Me, if you please. I asked them what in God's name they thought I would know about it. One of their men, the leader I suppose, said he had been at your dance. I thought at the time that you and Alec must have been out of your minds to let them in.'

Patiently Meli tried to explain that there had been no question of letting or not letting them in, but Emma still thought from a world where people came by invitation. 'This, Gran,' a name used at first by Robin, 'is 1921 and not 1901: but tell me, what was their reason for coming to Eila House?'

'Those men are out for blood, if I ever saw it. Out for the blood of the man or men who killed their Major whatever his name was. They actually wanted to search the house, if you please. I said 'over my dead body' and waved my stick in their faces.'

'Search for what?' Meli tried to sound casual, but her heart had started to pound.

'For the culprits, for anything that can lead them to a kill. They made wild statements about burning the whole of Rynah down and shooting everyone in it, if they didn't get co-operation. Jim Kernahan had already reported to Captain Clarke that his man has not reported for work since the affair and he passed the word on to this group that thought they would invade me today.'

To Meli, her voice sounded far away as she heard herself say, 'Was the name Martin?'

'Yes, that was the name.' Meli felt the arm she was still holding tense. 'How did you know? Have they been bothering you too?'

'No, not yet, thank God! But I remember Jim and Etta had a man called Martin on their houseboat, who was kind to Robin and took him perch fishing several times during the Raheen Regatta.'

How quickly could she get rid of the old woman, so that she could think? What could she do, if they arrived at Merlin and demanded to search the house? This was a new development, searching the big houses. So far only the cottages and barns of those who might be connected with wanted men had been entered. For this reason, Meli had made her rash offer to Con and he, on his part, had felt safe in bringing Martin to the Merlin potting shed.

At the greenhouse she tried to show her interest in the winter jasmine and then sat uneasily on a wooden bench.

'Really Gran, I think I'll have to go and lie down. My head is torturing me; maybe it's another migraine.' Meli had frequently suffered from these and mercifully Emma took the hint. She had got her news off her chest and, kissing her daughter-in-law, started home by the same path that Meli had herself taken not twenty-four hours earlier.

The doctor to the rescue

Con was in the yard and Meli led him into one of the stables. He had not heard of the army's visit to Eila, but he too had been uneasy all day after Ed's warning. There was, they decided, nothing they could do. Jim Kernahan had announced Martin's continued absence which, by recent order, he had been correct in doing, and the hunt would now be in deadly earnest. She could not turn Martin out to his certain death; and, if visited, she could only try to emulate her mother-in-law's stout defence of the privacy of her home. They agreed that they would not as yet tell Martin; but he must be warned that if, from now on, he heard men's voices he must remain absolutely still until she or Con came to visit him.

Dr. Lyster had mentioned casually to Meli the previous evening that he would be 'passing by' each day and again this might prove embarrassing, even dangerous. Why should a doctor be visiting any house daily unless someone was ill? She had the alibi in her hastily chosen excuse to old Emma. Con agreed that he knew she suffered with her head, indeed his mother and Ed had often spoken of it and felt sorry for her. Con must be sure and tell them of this new attack, and she would tell the servants that she felt another 'turn' coming on. This was how they described almost any ailment. She would also take additional steps to prove it, such as lying in a darkened room, asking Phoebe to bring her cold compresses and fetch her smelling salts from time to time.

As they returned to the house, Dr. Lyster's pony and trap came trotting up the drive. Meli waved and started discreetly up the steps, calling Con to ask the doctor to be sure and see her before he left. Taking the pony and trap round to the yard, Con came face to face with Mrs. Murphy, a basket of eggs in her hand.

'And what might you be doing, young man, ridin' around in the doctor's trap?'

'It's the Missus: she was in the garden a while back with the 'auld one' and felt one of her head troubles coming on. Sent me skipping across the wood to fetch the doctor, quick like that.'

Con felt proud of his lie. It fitted in with their recent plan, and would prevent a touchy Mrs. Murphy from wondering why she had not been allowed to know of her Mistress's ailment. He escaped by saying that he had to get over and shut the greenhouses up before the winter's frost killed all the plants. Watching Mrs. Murphy enter the house, he collected his basket from the stable and went quickly to the side door.

The doctor looked worried. He had finished dressing Martin's wound and stood by the camp bed stroking his chin. Then he spoke earnestly to Con.

'He needs help beyond that which I am able to give him; in fact, he should be got to a hospital.'

All three men knew that the nearest hospital to Merlin lay twenty-five miles west of Rynah. To try and take him there would be almost certainly disastrous. This was the area of the countryside that the Black and Tans were scouring and the hospital itself would be watched night and day for wounded men.

'Ah, shure I'll pull through, Doctor. Leave me here where it's quiet and safe,' was all Martin could say. If he knew what Con had just learned from Meli, he might not have felt so safe, even here in proud Merlin.

Dr. Lyster had cause to be worried. He too was committing

a crime in attending to this man who had been wounded by the bullet which he himself had extracted. Yet, he realised, as the other could not, that surgery was vital and urgent. It was Con who broke the silence.

'The Mistress wants to see you, Sir. She's having one of her head troubles.'

Dr. Lyster snapped his bag, wished Martin a good night's rest – he had purposely given him an extra sedative – and walked slowly up the stairs. In the smoking room, Meli greeted him and immediately noticed his worried look.

'You are a kind and generous man.'

'And you, Mrs. Casemond, are a kind and reckless woman. May I please have a whiskey and soda? I need to think. Oh, please excuse me. Con tells me you are suffering from – is it a migraine?'

As Meli poured the doctor's drink from Alec's cupboard, she laughed: '*Un malaise de convenance*', she said quietly, and then added: 'Forgive me, an expression my governess used for my miserable complaint. No doctor, it is a fabrication to cover our present problem.'

'Mrs. Casemond, may we talk frankly? This man's condition is serious. He may need surgery and only a hospital can provide it. Inshree is twenty-five miles from here, but the road will be watched. Really the country is in a deplorable state.' Dr. Lyster was old and had known Ireland in its better days.

The uncomfortable experience that Meli had had only that afternoon in the photographic room had not left her mind. She had found little time to think of it with Emma's surprise arrival and news, followed by her talk to Con. During the short time the Doctor was with Martin, she had been trying to steel herself to tell Con that the whole thing must stop. It was crazy, completely, absolutely. She was risking the reputation of herself and her family, even Merlin itself. The fact that she was English would only infuriate the Black and Tans should they find their quarry sheltered and nursed under her own roof. Meli was frightened, very frightened, but was it only Emma's news which was responsible?

The whole undertaking had got beyond her and now, in addition, there was this odd compelling feeling towards Martin. It had taken all her stern upbringing to force herself out of his presence. What indeed would the situation be, were he to stay on indefinitely? Almost gladly she welcomed the news that a hospital was needed, but it was accompanied by a sharp stab at the thought of his leaving Merlin.

The doctor continued: 'Although I managed to extract the bullet, it had previously done its work: the shoulder is badly damaged.'

The room had become almost dark, and Meli looked across at the old man who had brought many of Emma's flock into the world and whose present consulting room had been in existence for over forty years. Their problem was great and they could still wash their hands simply by telling Con. But what would that gawky, kindly, consumptive youth do with his burden. There was a tap at the door and Nellie, bringing in the oil lamp, carefully and dawdling slightly, closed the shutters and pulled the curtains. Nellie loved any kind of event, even if it meant the mistress having a migraine. At the door, she hung back, even though conversation had almost ceased while she did her work.

'Yes Nellie, what is it?'

'Con's after tellin' Mrs. Murphy about your head, Ma'am, and we're real sorry, Ma'am.'

'That is what the doctor and I are talking about. I may have to go and have some treatment.'

'Oh Ma'am, not in a hospital or somewhere?' Nellie's concern was tinged with excitement.

At Meli's statement, Dr. Lyster looked up in amazement. What was the woman talking about? Meli heard her own words and wondered where they came from.

'Yes Nellie, I may have to go to Dublin and get the wretched thing settled. Dr. Lyster was just discussing hospital, weren't you?' she added with a reassuring smile, knowing only too well that migraines were not settled. 'Go along now, there's a good girl and I will ring if I want anything. Tell Mrs. Murphy I'll let her know later about supper.'

Nellie skipped off happily. Now she really had some gossip to tell the kitchen.

'Mrs. Casemond,' he spoke sternly, 'if I understand what is on your mind – your plan I mean – then as a friend of your husband and his family, I would be most wrong in even letting you consider it.'

Once more fate had taken a hand. The subconscious mind works very rapidly, and Meli's response flowed forth: 'I have read the newspapers and I know what the new law from Dublin Castle says. We have both in our different ways taken on this, to say the least, unusual responsibility. I agree that Inishree is impossible, so what is left? If this were England where every town of size has its hospital, this man might stand a chance, but here ...' She raised her hand in a sign of helplessness. 'My husband will shortly be returning from England to Dublin; my son is at school there. Why should I not go there?'

'Why indeed! But what will that gain our invalid?' Dr. Lyster belonged to a generation who only took the train for long journeys.

Meli smiled. 'Travelling by train makes my migraine impossible. Do you not remember that since Alec bought the Vauxhall, I have full use of the Ford?' This was true; all the food supplies were fetched by her from Kahirloch and her journeys often took her further than the nearby village. The road to Dublin she knew only too well through her frequent visits with Alec. Meli's attitude to this strange situation was stiffening through the increasing crisis surrounding it.

'The journey will take four hours if I am lucky and we must get out of Merlin for all our sakes. Any Army doctor examining him will see immediately that he has received professional treatment.' It was a mean statement, but under the circumstances a practical one. There would not be much difficulty in tracking down where this help had come from. Without speaking Dr. Lyster rose and refilled his glass, an act he would not have dreamed of in other days.

'What do you propose, Mrs. Casemond?'

'Simply this. If you can arrange his admittance to a Dublin hospital, where he can avoid being discovered, I will endeavour to get him there safely.'

'But how in Heaven's name can you do it? You may be stopped at any bend in the road.'

Meli smiled. Although Martin was physically strong, he was of slight build and not more than five foot six inches in height.

'Doctor, we live in an age of motoring vehicles. He will be suitably dressed as my cook, who is suffering from appendicitis and must be taken urgently to hospital for an operation. You will give a letter to me stating this; and your signature, if you so wish, can be illegible. Doctors', in my experience, always are anyway!' she added with another smile, this time coupled with a note of plea.

'To keep him here though is still more dangerous, really most terribly dangerous,' she continued. 'Alec would never forgive me. No less than treating a wanted man in his own house.'

Dr. Lyster squirmed in his chair; he did not like or understand blackmail, but here was this elegant well-born woman stooping to – well his Victorian mind preferred to think of it as 'pressure'. It was really not attractive or wholesome in a woman and a lady. She had played a bold card in challenging him to even know of – let alone negotiate by telegram – a hospital who would take a man with Martin McCarthy's probable record. In his quandary, he realised that she would have been well within her right to challenge his presence here at Merlin, attending to Martin in the first place.

'I said you were a kind woman, but a reckless one and I repeat it. However, in the course of years, I have kept in touch with members of my profession in the capital and, if you insist, I think I know where he might receive the treatment which he urgently requires. To send a telegram from Kahirloch would be fatal. Clarke's men can demand to inspect them at any moment.'

Again Meli had the answer. In those days, private telephones in country districts were almost unknown; the telegram was cheap and reasonably fast.

'You write it and I will send it from the next county. On this I will give you my solemn promise. I think, Doctor, from what you said, there is no time to lose.' Again she was challenging his professional position.

From his black leather attaché case he took two sheets of paper. At Alec's desk he wrote on the first a telegram addressed to 'O'Connor, 270 Merrion Road, Dublin.' The message ran:

'Patient, old friend, needs treatment for respiratory difficulty, Lyster.'

At the second sheet, he paused and then wrote quickly. The letter was unsigned as far as Meli could see when he handed it to her and the writing looked like a complicated medical prescription, such as he had often given to her to take to the local chemist.

'Mrs. Casemond, I can only repeat that I think you are taking a very dangerous risk, and I appreciate your promise not to send the telegram until you are well clear of this district. Guard that letter carefully and give it only to the man to whom it is addressed.'

His drink finished, the old doctor turned to Meli: 'God go with you and guard you on your way. I hope I shall live long enough to see Ireland happy and contented once again.'

Early morning escape

Con was standing at the bottom of the steps holding the pony's bridle. They bid the doctor goodnight and went to the smoking room once more. There Meli told him of her plan. Con said little. He was a simple lad and had respect for his betters. Whatever the doctor and Mrs. Casemond decided must be right. Furthermore he was still living in terror of a surprise visit from the Black and Tans. To travel by night, they both realised would be hopeless; for that, as Con knew all too well, was when ambushes took place. Early in the morning, after daylight came, was the most hopeful time. In country districts, people rose late in winter-time; and whatever the military might have been up to during the night, they would hopefully be sleeping it off by then. From the Sinn Féin, Meli had for once little to fear. For them, in her new role, with Martin at her side, she could expect nothing but assistance. Trouble from the Black and Tans, if they were sober, was unlikely in the early morning, with her accent. She began to feel cheered, even excited. This was an event and she had lived alone so much at Merlin, both through the long war years and afterwards, that she felt at times the world was passing her by.

There was much to be done. Con must come early in the morning and prepare Martin and dress him with clothes she had yet to find. Martin, according to the doctor, had regained enough strength to be able, with Con's help, to reach the car. To tell Mrs. Murphy and the girls that she intended to act on Dr. Lyster's advice and go immediately to Dublin for treatment was quite logical; but it would oblige them all to fuss round her and help her into the car, carrying her bags and other belongings. That would never do. No, she must take an unusual line: simply leave a note explaining that, having suffered much pain during a sleepless night, she had decided to go straight away to Dublin without disturbing them. It was an unlikely tale, but would have to suffice.

There was a short path through some laurel bushes from the side door to the drive beyond the open gravel sweep. Here they would not be so easily seen from the house. Con would fill the car from Alec's petrol cans and leave it in the bushes on his way home; and then tomorrow, he would somehow creep out of the Gate Lodge early enough to see off the oddest cargo the Ford had ever carried. Merlin, in common with other country estates, had several approaches and one, only used by farm carts, wound its way through its fields to reach the road half a mile nearer Kahirloch. This she would use. Con would walk ahead and open gates to save using the main drive and thus avoid meeting with his mother or Ed, whose paternal eye in Alec's absence, guarded everything. Meli hoped to mislead any serious person en route to Dublin that Martin was her cook, but she could hardly do so on her own doorstep, where Mrs. Murphy was a well known character.

Both conspirators, without mentioning it, kept their ears alert for the dreaded sound of approaching army trucks; but probably Emma Casemond's firm reception of her unwanted visitors at Eila House that very day had served as a temporary discouragement.

To the regular Military, men like Captain Clarke, the thought of searching Eila House or Merlin was impossible; but to the Black and Tans, a nothing assortment of desperadoes, justifiably stung and infuriated by their loss, this delicacy might not come easily. All Ireland was a place of deep suspicion and mistrust towards these men who had been hastily recruited, ill clad and sent across the sea 'to raise hell if necessary'.

At five-thirty, Meli awoke. It was still dark and a chill wind blew through her bedroom windows. Con had promised to come and help Martin into the car at seven-thirty and, since his brother Ed came to work at eight-thirty in the winter months, the Ford must be well away before then. She dressed and went downstairs. No sound greeted her, except a sad sighing of wind in the bare chestnut boughs outside. Merlin possessed table lamps and hand lamps and the latter could be carried along corridors and into bathrooms. Meli had put one by her door the previous evening and now, lamp in hand, she went down to alert Martin. Con had returned to him the previous evening, after his talk with Meli, and had told him of Dr. Lyster's remarks and of Mrs. Casemond's plans to get him to hospital. Naturally, Martin was grateful for he, better than anybody, knew the risks that were being taken on his behalf. The door of the photographic room was ajar. In order to give him more air, Meli pushed it quietly open.

The soft yellow light from the oil lamp shone on Martin's sleeping face. Again Meli felt that wave, calmer now, sweep through her body. With the exception of her husband and Robin, this was the first time in her life that she had stood and watched a male form sleeping before her. Silently she sank into the only chair the room possessed and listened to his breathing. It was calm and even. Somewhere an owl cried and Martin turned and gave the sigh of a small child. His hand lay close to her. Automatically, she took it in hers and gently stroked it. This was not the way she had intended to awaken him; but some power, superior to hers, guided her movements.

How long she sat there in her husband's workroom she did not know; time for her had stopped and with it the life she had lived during these last years. Gently the grasp of the strong hand in hers tightened, but not a flicker of an eyelid showed that Martin was not still deep in sleep. Again Meli felt a wave descend through her body. Life was surely demented. Here she had planned a journey, fraught with danger, in order to save this man whose hand she held, and now, as she watched, the first wan light of winter's dawn beckoned her through the glass panels of the side door. Were this country into which she had chosen to marry not torn with strife, she could have languished in this calm, sweet, gentle scene eternally; but already she knew it was time to move, if her plan was to succeed. The strong hand in hers pulled her gently forward and the long black lashes hiding those rarely beautiful eyes flickered, as her lips rested on the forehead above them. Outside, gravel grated under the boots of a human foot. Gently Martin moved Meli's head with his left hand, until their lips met.

Moments later, the side door handle turned quietly and Con's tall thin figure stood silhouetted by the lamplight.

'Ma'am, they've been.' He looked pale as he spoke.

'What, Con, what happened?' she asked.

Martin's eyes were open now, but he remained silent.

'Last night. A car came to the Lodge. Ed said I was off getting the doctor for you. There were two men. They said I must report at the Barracks this morning at ten o'clock.'

The net was tightening and to leave too early might cause suspicion. A motor car on the roads near Kahirloch in the early twenties was a rarity. Even Dr. Lyster whose life was spent visiting remote cottages used only his pony and trap. Now Meli faced a worse predicament. To take Martin on this perilous drive meant leaving Con, her loyal employee, to await interrogation. If only she had never let herself become involved in this pathetic struggle to shake off the shackles which her country had maintained for seven centuries over this sweetly sad island. Well Con must talk his way out of his interrogation.

Together they dressed Martin in Meli's oldest clothes. Then Meli left to fetch her own suitcase. It was almost daylight – a sombre winter's morning which was to become the most eventful day of her life. The laurels were their meeting place and, as she walked along the little used path, her mind was filled with foreboding. Mad, mad, mad, was all she could think: to throw away her marriage, her home and respect, all on this one folly. Briefly her mind flashed back to her childhood house, those grey stone walls. Could they ever house a drama such as this? No indeed, for they lived in the wrong century for the quixotic act. But here in Ireland, life crept along at its own pace: one, two, how many centuries behind the bustling post-war world?

Con swung the handle, and the faithful Ford spluttered into life. Their journey had begun. At the farm gate, which stood nearest Kahirloch, Con wished them 'God speed'. Within two hours, he had his own ordeal to face; Meli gave him what advice she could.

'Remember, Con, I have been alone at Merlin, the Master is in England and I hate to be alone. You have done extra work during these last days, in and around the house. Indeed it was not possible for you to leave Merlin.' They waved farewell to each other as Martin sat silent, watching the thin rays of sunlight dart from behind heavy molten winter clouds.

The long winding village street was almost deserted; but, as the car chugged up the hill, there stood Mrs. Delaney despatching her two post boys with a sack of mail. That the postmistress was a gossip was well known: all postcards which came through her small office were read avidly over endless cups of tea. Already she was waving to stop Meli, which could mean that she had a telegram for her. This normally would have been delivered by Pat on his rounds; but here was Mrs.

Casemond driving away from Merlin on this early winter's morning.

Meli looked at Martin out of the corner of her eye. Her old black muffler was tethered firmly by one of her thickest motoring veils, and Alec's plaid coat came up to his chin, topped by a woollen scarf. It was the best disguise she could manage, but she did not trust its effectiveness in front of Mrs. Delaney's inquisitive gaze. The news that she had seen young Mrs. Casemond driving through the village with a 'rum one' would spread quickly and, in all likelihood, reach by some unfortunate coincidence the Barracks itself.

As the hill steepened the car slowed. Mrs. Delaney stepped forward, a telegram in hand. Quickly Meli changed to second gear and pressed the accelerator hard down. Over the noise of the engine she shouted: 'Keep it for me, I will be back.'

Mrs. Delaney drew back to avoid the mud splashing on her shoes; she looked surprised and scowled hard at the figure in the passenger seat. This was not the treatment to which she was accustomed for, in that remote country district, Mrs. Delaney's telegrams were equal in importance to gaily wrapped presents handed over by a benevolent Father Christmas.

Meli found that she was becoming used to taking quick decisions where Martin's welfare was concerned but, as this included her own, she had little choice. Further up the hill, a small road turned off to the left which led to the village of Pirone. It was highly unlikely, but just possible, that she would be visiting early on a winter's morning; but she realised that she must see what was in that telegram since it was probably from Alec about his return. Leaving the car and its passenger, she walked back to the small Post Office and gave Mrs. Delaney her warmest smile.

'The car is going so badly that I was afraid it would stop altogether on the hill. I have left it on the Pirone road which is level. Oh thank you so much.' Mrs. Delaney handed a telegram from over the counter. She allowed Meli to read it in silence.

'It will be nice for you to have Mr. Alec back. Merlin must be quite lonely without both of them.' She referred to Robin also. The telegram had been sent from Dublin on the previous evening; Meli's hand shook slightly as she read the four words:

'Arriving teatime love Alec.'

Mrs. Delaney appeared to be busily sorting her post.

'Yes, oh indeed it will. I miss them both greatly and the house is so quiet without Robin.'

A blown bridge bypassed

As she walked back up the hill towards the car, Meli realised that her fateful drive would now carry yet another hazard: not only the Military and the Sinn Féin, but now, most delicate of all, her husband. There were, no doubt, other roads which would bring them to Dublin, but this would involve considerable extra distances and who knew what state they would be in, for bridges were being blown up daily and trees felled. No, she must go on with her plan and trust in God's protection. Alec had said teatime, though he seldom gave specific times in his telegrams and it was now past nine o'clock. With luck, they should have covered the greater part of their journey by lunchtime, but so much depended on possible hold ups. A blown bridge could easily add an hour or more to their time. There were several already, but these were known to Meli from former journeys and, with care and advice from locals, she could negotiate them. In addition to her other worries, she was concerned about Martin's condition. As described by Dr. Lyster, gangrene was the imminent danger and not a moment should be wasted. Her car started on the first pull of the handle: how she blessed the old Ford, particular after other cars that she had seen including, on occasion, the Vauxhall itself.

At the post office in the small village of Letifrac, Meli paid two shillings and sixpence to send Dr. Lyster's telegram to Dublin – so much depended on its safe and speedy arrival.

As the miles ticked up on her speedometer, Meli began to feel more relaxed; also she was occupied in negotiating frequent potholes in the early stretches of the road. This lay across the great Bog of Allen which, from the beginning of Irish civilisation, had provided natural fuel for many a home. On both sides stood little stooks of peat sods, shaped as tripods so that wind could blow freely through them and in time dry out the water from these spongy dark loaves. An occasional donkey cart was all they met, for the day was grim and cold, and peat is cut in spring or summer time. Martin, whom Meli remembered from the *Christina* as gay and talkative, was now silent. She let him be.

After two hours driving, with Kahirloch and its connections far behind and several small towns safely passed, they stopped near the gates of an estate which Meli had often visited. She knew that it was now uninhabited as were many country homes, since the troubles had increased. Her thermos flask of strong sweet tea had kept its heat excellently and Martin smiled as she handed him his cup.

'You're a great lady, Ma'am.'

'Nonsense, but we are not going to risk detection in any of the pubs or hotels along the road. Last night I asked for a generous supper, which is packed in a lunch basket in the back. After Mrs. Murphy and the girls were in bed, I hardboiled some eggs on the kitchen range and remembered to take the box of biscuits from my study. I don't think Nellie will miss the two bottles of Guinness from the dining room sideboard either.' She had also filled one of Alec's flasks with whiskey in case Martin's condition worsened, but this she kept for emergency.

Refreshed, they drove in the direction of Maryborough. This town had long been associated with the army and possessed a sizeable Headquarters. Its name came from Queen Mary, wife of William of Orange, and recalled one of the blackest chapters in Ireland's history. It was a busy town and one that Meli would gladly have avoided, since checkpoints were erected without warning. Two women travelling alone might not create much suspicion, but what if Martin was questioned? His voice was deep, and the heavy muffler and veil might not be adequate shields from a watchful sentry. During the journey, she had tried desperately to think of an alternative route but without success.

Martin had dozed off and Meli felt almost happy. Somehow they would surmount difficulties and Martin would pull through. Dr. Lyster's contact would operate on his damaged shoulder and he would be well again. But ... Meli felt a twinge at her heart when she realised that he could never return to Rynah. Jim Kernahan had seen to that. She took her eyes off the road for a moment to look at the disguised and huddled figure beside her.

Only just in time did her eyes return to the windscreen, for the car was approaching a bridge under which flowed a small river well in spate, one of many rivers that sprawl across the countryside. With foot and hand brake applied at full strength, the car stopped abruptly within yards of a gaping hole. The centre of the bridge had been blown away and, judging by the others Meli had seen, this looked new work. For Martin now aroused, it was a new experience. Sabotage was carried out by his party to inconvenience others not themselves. Here he was a wounded man and almost helpless, urgently in need of medical care, gazing at the fast flowing river which stood between them and that very care. Meli wished that she had those planks which Alec carried on his car for such emergencies, but then it took a strong man to place them correctly, and Martin was in no condition to help.

After several minutes, Meli spotted a boy peering at them through the hedge beyond the bridge. Automatically, Meli put a restraining hand on Martin's arm, as she had done several times with her husband. It had been agreed that Martin would speak to no one throughout the journey. She opened her door and called to the boy.

'Can you get help? My friend is very ill and I have to get him – her to Dublin quickly.' The boy just stood and stared vacantly at the car. It had become the sport of youngsters to watch the discomfort of travellers at unexpected hazards. Meli tried again:

'Do you know if there is any other way round? I must get on. Do please get help.' The boy continued to stare, then wiped his nose with the back of his hand and disappeared back through the hedge. He had not spoken a word.

Martin had been to Dublin with Colonel Kernahan, but not recently, and he did not know the road as well as Meli. The sharpness with which she had brought the car to a stop had jolted his shoulder and it was obvious that he was now in pain. Quickly from the back seat, she lifted the lunch basket and poured him a measure of straight whiskey. He drank it, gave a slight shudder and smiled: 'You're a great little lady, Ma'am.' It was the word 'little' that carried the tenderness of what he felt.

A man drew level with the car and stood by Meli's window. He had sharp features, and his suspicious black eyes surveyed the inmates of the car. By his clothing he was a local small farmer, and his raincoat was stained and torn at the collar. Who knew what part, if any, he had in this recent act of sabotage, which it was well known was done chiefly to inconvenience the Military and not ordinary travellers. Again Meli told her story, as she had to the boy ten minutes earlier. Her friend was sick and must get to Dublin quickly. Could he help by suggesting an alternative route? The man was staring hard at Martin, who in turn was now staring back through the thick motoring veil. Before the stranger could reply to Meli's plea, Martin, who had pulled himself up in his seat, shouted across Meli.

'Sean O'Sullivan, if you don't get this car across that bloody stream and quick at that, I'll skin the hide of you, as sure as me name is Martin McCarthy.' As he spoke he pulled up the veil with his good hand and smiled at Sean.

'By the Holy Mother of God, and it's yerself Martin. What ails ye?'

'What ails me man is being stuck here wasting time and this lady tryin' to get me to Dublin for me shoulder.' The slight wink and the ridiculous clothes which he was wearing told Sean all he needed to know. Martin's shoulder had not been damaged by any natural cause. 'Sit easy Ma'am, and keep this old codger quiet, while I run and fetch help.' And Sean was off back the way he had come.

'He's a pal of mine and a good one at that.' Martin wished that he could tell her that they had trained together secretly as volunteers, but that was out of the question and, furthermore, he suspected that Mrs. Casemond would not embarrass him with questions. She did not.

When Sean and a friend returned, followed by the boy, it was noon. The other touched his cap to Meli and gave a greeting she did not understand to Martin.

'If you'll turn the car, Ma'am, and follow us.'

A short distance back a gate in the hedge stood open. The field beyond was muddy but a track lay across it to another gate which had also been opened. At the far end of the second field stood a thatched whitewashed cottage where chickens scattered in front of the car, and a large collie dog barked loudly at their approach. In front of the low door, a woman waited.

'I'm Mrs. Claffey. And it please you Ma'am, the kettle's on the boil.' She was a pretty woman and her smile was welcoming. The men were talking to Martin. 'Bedad and we'll have you out of there in a jiffey.'

Gently they helped Martin from the car and into the cottage. Meli followed with the woman behind her. Inside burned a bright turf fire and on the hob sat a big black teapot. In a saucepan nestling amongst the cinders sat four brown eggs. Mrs. Claffey started to cut some thick slices of home-made bread. The two men nodded to Martin and left the cottage.

'Yes, it was terrible about the bridge indeed.' The woman looked and sounded really dismayed as she spread golden farmhouse butter on the bread. Martin was seated on a heavy wooden settee near the fire; he spoke little but seemed contented.

When the two men returned, Mrs. Claffey's generous meal was finished; conversation had been quite general: the poor weather, the news from Dublin and many details concerning her farmyard. It was obvious that all three were at pains not to touch, even remotely, on any delicate subject.

'And now, Ma'am, if you're ready. Martin, stay here a while.'

Meli left the cottage as bidden. Outside Sean spoke again. 'Take a look first, Ma'am, till you see whether it is strong enough.'

At the end of the farmyard flowed the stream, which, lower down, had been the cause of their delay. Across it lay a simple footbridge; but beside it now, in addition, strong planks reached from side to side. This in the past had been Alec's job, but there was nothing for it now but that she should try and drive over the stream herself.

''Twill be easier on the planks without Martin; we'll bring him over later.' It was the second man who spoke.

Successfully Meli negotiated the stout planks, having first thanked Mrs. Claffey for her kindness.

''Tis nothin', Ma'am, nothin' atall I assure you. God speed you now and get this poor creater on to Dublin.'

Carefully Martin was returned to his seat. The meal and the rest had done him good. They traversed two more soggy fields before reaching the Dublin road. At the parting, both men doffed their caps to Meli; they knew what she was doing for one of their lot.

Maryborough presented no problems. It was market day and the town was busy and full with pony traps and farm carts. The road ahead of them was tarmacked and Meli could increase her speed. It was two o'clock and with luck they would reach the capital by four. Where was Alec, Meli thought, as mile followed mile? This was the road she had learned from him, and if he had lunched in Dublin, which was more than likely, their paths must inevitably cross. Martin dozed again; he knew nothing of the telegram.

Several convoys passed by, soldiers hanging on to the metal roof struts. No one questioned the two veiled women in their Ford Sedan. The Curragh was not far ahead – another section Meli dreaded. In happier days, she and Alec had often broken their journey and stayed overnight with Jim Millar, bosom friend of Harry Casemond of Drumalla, Alec's brother. There they had received generous hospitality which did much to soften the journey to and from Merlin. Now with her strange companion this could not be. Indeed, if she were stopped and found herself in trouble, she would not dream of using Jim Millar's name as a friend, for he still wore the King's uniform.

Hospital is reached

The main road ran straight across the Curragh, a flat open area with no hedges. It was the headquarters of the British Army, the Aldershot of Ireland. Instinctively, Meli felt the nearness of Alec's presence. Unless he had changed his plans, which was unlikely as he had sent the telegram, they must soon meet. What then? As her husband, Alec could do little to her; but he could make trouble for Martin. It would be easy to turn him in here as the whole area was a hornet's nest of Military, which probably by now had Martin's name provided by Captain Clarke on their 'wanted for questioning' list.

Meli gently pulled the car off the road, and stopped the engine while Martin slept. She took off her scarf and wrapped it round the front number plate. It was a calculated risk, for any sentry could stop her, but the risk at that moment seemed less than her husband doing so. To the sentry she might get away with it by saying her radiator was leaking – motor cars in 1921 were still unpredictable.

The empty Curragh yawned before them, and her premonition of danger grew alarmingly. Half way across a road turned off to the right and this led to the Camp where Jim Miller was billeted. The road surface was good and Meli increased her speed. If only she could reach the hedged road at the far end. As she approached the road leading to the camp, a watery afternoon sun shone momentarily upon the outline of a long low car. It was travelling fast and Meli knew who was at the wheel. Alec's Vauxhall 30/98 was at that time almost unique in

Ireland and its lines were not to be confused with other cars. Her only hope was to pass the intersection before the Vauxhall reached it. If only the power of the two cars were reversed! She gave the Ford its full acceleration and pulled her coat collar high up round the neck. Martin had slouched down in his seat and was hardly visible, she hoped. As the cars drew level, Meli realised that, at the speed she was now travelling, this was probably a better place to face her ordeal than some narrow stretch of road, where they would have to stop and discuss her extraordinary and unannounced journey. Alec had stopped to give way at the main road; he looked hard at Meli who stared ahead. Out of the corner of her eye, she noticed that Alec had a passenger, a female. As the Ford shot passed the stationary Vauxhall, Meli realised that her husband's companion was Etta Kernahan. Her relief at reaching the Dublin end of the Curragh was sufficient to allow her to brush aside for the moment the presence of Etta at Alec's side. That was for another day. Perhaps she too had been visiting Jim Millar. Martin was now the important person. What his presence had meant to her in these critical days she had not allowed herself to think on, but now, as they neared Dublin, the thought that she must part from him shot through her like a knife wound. No longer did she care about the rights and wrongs of her recent actions. The man sleeping beside her had become part of her life, regardless of his class or political beliefs. In addition, he was now helpless, and this only touched her heart the more.

At four o'clock, they passed Mountjoy Jail, where languished many Sinn Féin prisoners. Meli pursed her lips. Martin would not be its guest if she could help it. Trams and street lights brought her comfort after the long miles of empty open road. Martin shifted his position and sighed. How thankful she would be to deliver him safely to Merrion Road. Twenty minutes later, having lost her way twice owing to a heavy shower, she drew up before the number given to her by Dr. Lyster.

The Victorian red brick house looked sombre with steep flight of steps leading up to a stout front door. On the right, one window showed a chink of light through the heavy curtains. As she walked up the steps, tired now from her journey, Meli prayed that Dr. O'Connor was behind those curtains and had received her telegram. She pulled on the bell knob and heard the tinkling reply echo through the house. After a few moments, the door was opened by an elderly woman, who stared hard at Meli, her veil now thrown back over her hat.

'Yes, what can I do for you?' The voice was sharp, as Meli handed Dr. Lyster's personal note to the woman.

'My doctor, Doctor Lyster, sent a telegram this morning to Dr. O'Connor. Is he in?'

The woman looked at her. 'Why was it not sent from Kahirloch?'

Meli realised that she was being cross-questioned. 'I sent it on the way here. It was too late for Dr. Lyster to send it last night and when I left early this morning our Post Office had not opened.'

'Step into the hall please.' The statement was a command. The door closed behind them. Again the older woman challenged. 'Why have you taken so long to get here? My husband expected Dr. Lyster's patient by noon.'

At this Meli smiled. 'If you only knew what I have been through to get here at all!'

The woman relaxed. 'Where is the patient?' She spoke as if she had held a senior nursing position at some stage in her life.

'He is in the car outside and desperately needs treatment. We have been travelling since dawn.'

'Can he walk?' The question was so abrupt and it did not fit in with a person said to be suffering from a respiratory difficulty.

'Not alone, he is too weak and has to be helped.'

'Take your car round to the back, first street on the left and then left again. I will open the garden door. My husband will be back any minute. Neither you nor your patient must be seen outside this house. Hurry!' She opened the front door and, as in a dream, Meli walked down the steps.

Martin was awake and, by the white street lights, looked miserable. She climbed in beside him.

'It's alright. We've made it and the doctor will be here in a few minutes. We are going round to the back to wait for him. It's safer there.'

The street behind Merrion Road was less well lit; but the garden door, left ajar by Mrs. O'Connor, showed Meli where to park her car.

Quietly they sat in the car. Martin had removed the gloves she had provided. Gently, he took her hand in his. A warm glow flowed between them. Desperately, Meli was searching for a way to keep in touch with him. Any moment now, they would be parted and she might never see him again. Danger had brought them so close together; her heart ached as it had not done since she had left for New Zealand years before. She even thought of using Robin as a contact at his school, but this was ridiculous. How could a small boy be trusted with such a dangerous secret and anyhow he would have to convey any news to her in his Sunday letters. These were read by both his headmaster and Alec. No, there was no solution.

'Me darlin', if I pull though this lot, I'll lay me life at your feet, for I owe it to you already.' He pulled her towards him and kissed her tenderly on her cheek.

The garden door opened and an elderly man stood looking

up and down the street.

Through the open window of the car he spoke: 'We will bring him into the house. There are no steps on this side.'

Slowly and painfully on the doctor's arm, Martin entered 270 Merrion Road, followed by Melissa Casemond. They put him in a small garden room and left him there, while Meli followed the elderly man upstairs. They sat down in the softly lit dining room.

'Your name please, madam?' Meli told him. 'Dr. Lyster writes that his condition is serious?'

'Yes, it is his shoulder.'

Dr. O'Connor did not raise his eye from the table as Meli spoke.

'I cannot take him to a hospital tonight. It would be very dangerous. Only emergency cases are admitted and each one is scrutinized. He will be safe here in my care until tomorrow. You may have noticed a divan in the garden room. My wife is a highly skilled nurse. And now I must go and attend to him. You will no doubt wish to know of his progress. Do you intend to remain long in Dublin?'

'Yes, for a few days. My son is at school here and I must visit him.'

'Then call here tomorrow evening at seven. Do not bring your car and please use the garden door.'

They walked downstairs and past the garden room. Through the open door Meli could see Martin, but she did not stop. They had said their goodbye in the car and, in addition, Mrs. O'Connor was already at her work. At the gate the doctor bid her good night in a friendly manner and hoped that, with the pills he had just given her, she would pass a peaceful night.

Standing close by the car in this wet Dublin back street, there came to Meli the first symptoms of reaction from the unreal life she had lived since she stood in the thin moonlight and heard the curlew's call near Merlin's potting shed. She started the car and looked once more at the gate through which she had come back into the world of reality. How like Merlin it was, a gate for a side door and a garden room in place of Alec's photographic room. There was one difference, however: at Merlin she had watched over and protected her beloved guest; now she had handed over that responsibility and sat alone on a black chill January night a hundred miles from her home.

The mistress is missing

Alec Casemond stood on the platform of Westland Row Station and whistled to a porter: 'Put these in a cab and tell the driver to take me to the Shelbourne; I want to buy a paper.'

He had taken the night train and mail boat from London via Holyhead and Kingstown.

As the horse clip-clopped along the wet streets, Alec, looking out of the grubby cab window, realised that, although London was a fine and exciting city, Dublin meant more to him. The rows of Georgian houses had a serene and ageless look and maintained an almost touching dignity.

The Shelbourne receptionist received him warmly. She was elderly and had been sitting in her small mahogany-fronted office since Alec was a boy. Of course he could have a room and a bath, in order to change and freshen up. Indeed she was glad he had had a good crossing. Dear, dear! Last week visitors had arrived at the hotel with the grimmest stories of storms so violent that they thought the ship would capsize. One lady was so ill that she spent two days in bed in the hotel instead of travelling on to her home in Cork.

Half an hour later, much refreshed, he walked into the dining room. The Shelbourne was famous for its breakfasts. Real Irish sausages were accompanied by equally delicious rashers and fried eggs. With the marmalade, he turned to the paper he had bought at the station. Much of the news was similar to what he had read in the London evening paper. As he glanced across the headings with little interest, his eye was caught by one that caused him to put his toast down quickly:

'Rynah Ambush – Search for culprits proceeds – Man named'

His eye ran quickly down the column: 'The authorities at Kahirloch have received information that a Rynah man, Martin McCarthy, has been missing since the night of Major McTaggart's murder. His mother, when questioned, gave no helpful information, merely weeping and stating that her son was a wild gossoon and never told what he'd be at! The search continues.'

Alec sat back in his chair and rubbed his chin. Martin McCarthy, Raheen Regatta, the *Christina* and ...

A pair of soft, scented hands folded from behind over his eyes: 'And what are you doing having breakfast in the Shelbourne all by yourself?' The familiar voice cooed in his ear.

'Etta, sit down and read this, or maybe you know it already.'

Etta Kernahan read the short column and pouted, then smiled across coyly at Alec: 'Well, anyhow he was every inch the gentleman when he found us er .. kissing on the *Christina*. I hope they don't find him. Those Black and Tans shouldn't burst into people's houses and make themselves so unpopular. Of course, Jim would be furious if he heard me. He thinks that every Sinn Féiner should be smoked out and shot.'

Alec learned that Etta knew little more of events at Rynah or Kahirloch than he did. She had left the day after the Merlin dance to stay with friends in Galway, from where she had come up to Dublin. Of course, she knew about the ambush, but Ardmore lay to the west of Rynah on the Galway road. While she was trying to pack, her husband came in and out with wild stories he had picked up from Rynah villagers; and he had finally kissed her and gone hurrying off to pour out all he knew to his friend Captain Clarke.

As she finished her story, Alec glanced at the column again: 'Have received information'. This would go badly for Jim Kernahan, if Martin were caught and shot. But then Jim was always rushing round shouting at someone; he had spent too many years in India.

'Why don't we stay the night here?' suggested Etta.

Alec smiled but shook his head. He had sent his telegram to Meli from Kingstown pier, when the boat docked at seven o'clock; that was if the dumb looking porter, to whom he entrusted it with a generous tip, remembered to take it up the street to the Post Office. She would have it by now. A day and a night with Etta in Dublin would have been fun, great sport, but he had already spent longer in London than originally planned.

'No Etta, not this time, I can't. Meli will have had my wire and would only ask a mass of questions if I stayed overnight in Dublin. I tell you what ... Let me drive you back. I hate that damned journey alone. How about it?'

And so it was that Alec and Etta Kernahan, who had stopped to lunch at the Curragh with Jim Millar, watched the Ford Sedan pass them at speed heading for Dublin.

'That's dashed like our car. Could almost have sworn it was. Did you notice the number?'

'No. I'm afraid I wasn't looking, but I think there were two women in it.'

'Come to think of it, there seemed to be something hanging over the number plate – probably part of a torn radiator muff. Oh well! Ours isn't the only Ford on the road, like this beauty.' Alec patted the steering wheel of his beloved Vauxhall, put the car into gear and headed West.

In Maryborough, they were delayed by Sinn Féin's latest act of sabotage but, with a versatility which had now become almost second nature for travellers, they found an alternative route. Consequently daylight was waning as they reached Ardmore Castle and Alec refused the proffered hospitality.

Jim Kernahan, grateful for his wife's safe return, was overflowing with news. His own employee, Martin, thanks to his own information, was now the leading quarry in the district. A massive search was accompanied by increasing threats of reprisal. Alec was surprised and shocked to learn of the visit paid by the Black and Tans to his mother's home. This was a new and alarming development in the bitter struggle for supremacy.

In Dublin, he had been told of the rapid increase of volunteers to the I.R.A. cause. The City's streets showed clear evidence of an equal expansion of forces arriving from Britain. Jim Kernahan had no wish to see the administration change over into the hands of Local Government, as this would mean that the country, and those living in it, would be run by a bunch of Paddies. What had been good enough for his ancestors was good enough for him and he would do everything in his power to maintain it.

Alec passed the gates of Eila House. He would like to have called to see his mother, but it was already dark and he must think of Meli. She too had been living alone at Merlin while he had been in London. In front of Merlin Gate Lodge stood Ed; he sprang forward to open the gates, his face in the piercing headlights looked white and drawn.

'Sir, it's good to see you back. They've searched the big house and taken Con for questioning.'

Alec Casemond switched off the engine. He did not like what he heard. 'Who has searched Merlin? What do you mean? Where was the Mistress when this was going on? Didn't she show them off?'

'That's the trouble Sir. She had gone this morning before I got to my work. It must have still been dark and none of us heard the Ford come this way. No one can open the gates without my mother hearing it, sleeping as she does in the front room. The Mistress left a note for Mrs. Murphy saying her headache was so bad she was going to Dublin for treatment. That's all we know. At ten o'clock, a truckload of Black and Tans arrived, said they 'had evidence', took Con and went to search the big house. I tried to prevent them, but Phoebe had the front door open and a big chap said he'd stick his rifle butt in me stomach if I wanted to give them any trouble. Then they combed the house for God knows what. Got mad when they didn't find what they were looking for and drove off with me brother, saying they knew how to get information out of him.'

As Ed stood there helpless and shattered, Alec felt his world closing in around him like a steel knot. Why had his wife left in the dawn without the O'Tooles hearing him pass? Why was his home being searched and for what? Why had Con, who had worked for him and his family since a boy, been roughly taken from his work with threats? He thanked Ed for his information and patted him on the shoulder:

'You did your best. Do not be worried, we'll get Con back alright. Go back inside now and I'll see you in the morning.'

The Black and Tans have visited

As he drove down the avenue of naked beeches, standing black
against the winter sky, Alec wished he could take his rifle and
pay a visit to the bloody Black and Tans. At the garage, Mrs.
Murphy appeared from the back door holding an oil lamp
above her head. Alec walked towards her.

'Thank God it's you, Sir. Such going on I never believed
I'd have to stand and see.' It was plain that she had been
weeping. Alec pulled a chair up to the old fashioned kitchen
range and greeted the two housemaids, who had now appeared
looking as if they had both seen poltergeists.

'Ed told me you had visitors.'

'Visitors!' Mrs. Murphy sniffed and almost spat with fury
into her well polished grate. 'Human devils, that's what they
were. Barged into the house as if they owned it. Said they had
information. 'Information' I said and what may that be? They
sniggered and believe it or not Sir, as true as I'm standing here,
they actually pushed me out of the way.'

When Phoebe tittered, Mrs. Murphy drew herself up:
'And that'll be enough from you two idiots. A lot of good you
were in guarding the house that feeds you.'

'Phoebe, go and get a glass of whiskey please and bring
one to Mrs. Murphy.' Alec knew that his red-faced cook,
outraged in his absence, had a soft spot for a drop of Jameson.
When Phoebe returned, he put his feet on the kitchen table and
raised his glass. 'Thank you for stopping them from burning
the house down; they are not above that you know.'

Mrs. Murphy sipped her glass and drew up a chair. 'It was

THE BLACK AND TANS HAVE VISITED

terrible, Sir, them rogues would stop at nothing, even rape.'
She gulped as she used the dreadful word. 'Through the house
they went like a bunch of hornets. Opened drawers, looked in
cupboards. With that lot nothing is sacred.'

'And what did they hope to find?' Alec asked the question
nonchalantly.

'Only they and the Devil know, Sir, but they left mutterin'
amongst themselves about evidence to prove that 'he' had been
here.'

'And who is this 'he'? Did they tell you that?'

'Well Sir, not actually, but since you've been in England,
they've been hoppin' mad to find someone connected to that
Rynah affair after 'our' dance. It seems Colonel Kernahan
reported one of the Ardmore men missing from work – Martin
McCarthy, Sir, if you know the name.'

Alec knew the name only too well. He would like to have
spoken warmly of him, but these were not the times to enthuse
over anyone who might be considered 'wanted'.

Mrs. Murphy, warmed by her whiskey, was now anxious to
talk: 'Gossip has it Sir, that 'they' found blood on the barracks
step the night of the … er … hold up. The men in one of the
lorries that burst in on our dance heard a cry of pain and knew
that someone was wounded. Now, it's Martin they're after and
they can't get hold of him. The Devil hides his own.' Mrs.
Murphy was also being careful in her choice of epithet for
Martin's protector.

'Why in Heaven's name should they think he might be here
at Merlin?'

So recently returned from London, with dinner at
Romano's and evenings at the Empire and Alhambra in
Leicester Square, all this sounded like a fairy tale. His question
was greeted with that nervous silence which is significant when
children are asked awkward questions by their elders.

'Well Sir, it's like this. It seems they happened on an old bog hole up yonder at Firgrove Wood.'

Alec took his feet off the table and sat up in his chair. 'Yes, go on, what bog hole?'

Mrs. Murphy described the damp cavern which he and his brothers had dug in their childhood, the scene of so many youthful adventures; he had not thought of it for years.

'Inside, they claimed was evidence, damning evidence.' Mrs. Murphy's words trailed into silence and were followed by a sob. The white apron was lifted to shield the tears.

Alec was surprised and embarrassed. What was this hard old harridan weeping about? He waved towards the maids, clearly showing that they should disappear, but Mrs. Murphy, who was already wiping up the damage to her red face, sighed:

'Ah, sir, 'tis of no consequence; they already know, and the whole country will soon. They found some belongings of a Rynah youth called,' she paused, 'Kevin, and they are after him now.'

'Well, it's this way,' she again chose her words carefully. 'Young Kevin came from Dublin and he brought a document with him for Martin. By an unholy mischance didn't the Tanners find, or so they say, a bit of it in the bog hole. That took them hot foot to Eila House, where the Mistress showed them off with a stick. Later they came on here and no one but me and Ed to say a word to them. At first they were reasonable, but two of them disappeared off to the garden. After a while, there was great 'clobber' and they came running back with some kind of stretcher they'd found. I heard a fella' callin' out: 'There's blood on it'. After that they shouted at us as if we were cattle and tore all over the house and stable yard. Then they left, calling out 'traitors, we'll be back' followed by a lot of terrible words.' Nellie and Phoebe nodded their heads furiously. 'At the Gate Lodge, they threw Con in along with them. Since then we've all been worried out of our minds, scared to death and waiting for yourself or the Mistress to return.'

'Didn't you know I was returning today?'

'No sir, the Mistress didn't say a word.'

'But, didn't she receive my telegram? I sent it from Dublin early this morning.'

'Well Sir, that's the strange thing; she, the Mistress, left here without a word to any of us – just this little note.' Mrs. Murphy groped in the bosom of her apron and produced a much fingered piece of Merlin writing paper. It was in Meli's hand and ran: 'Dr. Lyster wants me to have treatment for my migraine and so I shall leave for Dublin early tomorrow morning. Please don't worry. M.C.'

Alec put the note down on the table and stared at it. This was not Meli's usual way of giving information to her staff. She was always most explicit and careful never to let Mrs. Murphy feel out of things. Her cook, particularly since Miss Livingstone's departure, had become a central figure in the sleepy old house.

'Not even Ed or his mother saw or heard her go.' The statement brought Alec back with a jolt. Something, perhaps many things were wrong and yet he couldn't put his finger on anything. He wished he had never gone off to London with Harry. Within the day, his wife had left mysteriously, his home had been searched, followed by threats, and one of his staff carried off by the enraged and vindictive Black and Tans who so recently had been his uninvited guests.

He stood up: 'I'll get to work on it tomorrow. Meantime, I'm darned hungry.' He tweaked the cook's tear-stained cheek. 'Come along now, you bunch of females. How about giving me some supper?'

His changed tone was contagious and the three women bustled round thankfully to have a lead at last. Nellie rushed ahead to light oil lamps, and Phoebe scurried off to lay the dining room table. Alec lingered on. To the older woman leaning over her range, he said: 'This is very serious. I don't like any of it. Pray God the Mistress is alright.'

Mrs. Murphy put down her spatula and crossed herself: 'Pray God she'll be protected in these wicked times.' Their eyes met over the table lamp.

'Why did you cry when you told me of young Kevin in Firgrove Wood?'

'He is my nephew, Sir, my sister's only child.' She stopped; her face over the lamp looked haggard. 'He may have done you and yours harm and me knowing nothing at all about it, except that he was studying in Dublin.' She looked as if she would weep again.

He smiled at her. 'These are strange times Ellen,' he said softly. 'Country against country, family against family. Whatever happens, I know that neither you nor yours would ever intend to harm my family.' He patted her hand and left the kitchen.

After supper, Alec unpacked; he was restless and did not want to sleep yet. The house, as he walked through the main rooms, did not look much disturbed. After all, the Black and Tans had been looking for a man and not money or jewels. They did not need to turn out chests of drawers. Obviously, the maids had done fine work in putting everything back in place. The drink cupboards in his smoking room were empty, as were the cigarette boxes. Two locked cupboards had been broken open and a padlocked door in the attic smashed.

The maids were exhausted from their worrying day; he quickly shooed them off to bed and the house was now very quiet; even Scram was with Ed at the Gate Lodge. Taking a box of photo plates from his dressing table, he walked downstairs. These were the pictures he had taken in London and he was curious to see how they would come out. Why not develop them now, when he knew tomorrow would obviously be confused? A small hand-lamp would do to guide him to the developing room. The door was ajar and he pushed it open carelessly, thinking that one of the girls might, in his absence, have given it one of its rare clean ups. His knee struck a hard object and he almost dropped the lamp. Holding it down whilst rubbing his shin, Alec saw below him in this little used room a camp bed. On it lay two rumpled blankets and to his amazement – Robbie's pillow.

Much had been happening in his home whilst he made merry across the water.

Return to face the music

It was not the Shelbourne to which Meli drove after her work at Merrion Road was completed. There, for certain, she would meet friends, the last thing she required at the moment. Alone with her thoughts in the Standard Hotel, Harcourt Street, Meli wondered whether her actions during these last two days had really only been a dream. The war years at Merlin had followed a tranquil pattern, during which she had probably become dull. The troubles confined social life to a minimum. Then without warning, a chance walk in the moonlight had changed her world. What would now become of her? Where did her road lie?

Dr. O'Connor had thoughtfully offered her a sedative, saying that such an arduous journey was likely to disturb her night's rest. Sitting on the side of her brass bedstead, she swallowed the white pill; her other hand held a glass of water. As she raised it to her lips the platinum wedding ring shone in the bright electric light. Was it mocking or reprimanding her for this day's work?

The telephone was answered promptly. Yes, it was Mr. Brooks speaking! He was glad that Mrs. Casemond had telephoned. The school had its little trouble: one of those seasonal events he reassured her – an epidemic of chicken pox, so infectious, really very tiresome. No, Robin had been fortunate so far, but of as Mrs. Casemond was in Dublin she might think it wise to take Robin home for a short time until the epidemic had run its course.

In fact, Mr. Brooks had a larger problem than he was prepared to confide to a parent of one of his pupils. The small sick bay was already overcrowded and, if any more contracted the disease, it would mean ambulances and the experience of a hospital isolation wing.

Meli's mind worked in perfect harmony with Robin's harassed headmaster. She had never felt so lonely and longed for Robin's company. Hourly her dread of returning to Merlin increased. What could she say to Alec or Mrs. Murphy? She had probably seriously hurt the latter's motherly feelings.

'Yes, well of course, I would be happy to; if you don't think it would hurt his studies. Yes, of course, he may bring his books with him. Our local vicar enjoys coaching and I'm sure would be glad if Robin bicycled over to the Rectory three or four times a week.' Her heart jumped with joy. What a marvellous stroke of fate. Robin would now return with her on the long journey and bring his bright cheerfulness, so sorely needed, back to Merlin.

The Ford, it seemed, had an extra zest as it bounced along through Donnybrook and onto the Bray road. Mrs. Brooks, a motherly woman, had packed Robin's suitcase. 'We'll let you know by wire as soon as this wretched epidemic has passed,' she called, waving to the departing car.

Robbie too was excited, and plied his mother with questions. He had hated leaving Merlin to start his second term. The first was exciting and unknown, but his return sitting in the Vauxhall next to his father was a dismal anti-climax. With so much mystery surrounding Merlin – the dance with its surprising and exciting guests; the Rynah ambush followed by Con's reticence – all had combined to make him resent leaving home for a restricted life with boys who thought mostly of dominoes and schoolboys' weekly magazines. Now, thanks to Terry Winthrop, who had become covered with pink blotches in the dormitory overnight, he found himself sitting at his mother's side driving into Dublin. Terry would enjoy a large slice of Robin's weekly walnut cake when they were all back in their Spartan dormitory.

Meli had already decided, after a good night's sleep, that she must not delay her return. She owed it to her husband, whom she had brazenly passed on the Curragh road. She also owed it to her staff, who could easily think she had become deranged for leaving them in such a callous manner. What of Dr. Lyster, that good Samaritan, who put his calling above political strife? Well, she would say that away from Merlin, her migraine had receded surprisingly. A telephone call to Robin's school had resulted in a plea from his headmaster to remove the boy immediately. Dr. Lyster, who had shown such understanding, would, she hoped, be her support in her story.

Robin too was anxious to get home. At Maryborough, she drove straight to Military H.Q. Yes, the bridge had been repaired sufficiently to allow private cars to pass. The duty officer wished her a safe journey.

As darkness fell, the Ford drew to a halt at the gates of Merlin. They were chained and padlocked, but the Gate Lodge had a light in the parlour window.

'Robbie darling, fetch Mrs. O'Toole please.' The boy was out of the car like a rocket. He knew the O'Tooles' back door better than his mother did and maybe, as it was almost dark, Con – his Con – might already be home. In this he was disappointed: pushing open the door, he found Mrs. O'Toole alone, sitting before a dying fire. She pulled herself up and took the keys off the dresser. Mrs. O'Toole came from a generation who showed modest but respectful courtesy to her betters. As she unlocked the gates, Meli was shocked to see the wan expression on her face.

'Mary, what is it? What's happened?'

'Oh, Ma'am, there's been terrible goings on since you left. They've raided the place and taken me boy. The Master bought the padlock and chain and told me no one was to pass through the gates.' Meli switched off the engine. It was better that she should have her briefing before she faced her husband.

'Is my husband at home?' The question was direct.

'No, Ma'am, he's off with Captain Clarke.'

'Then let me come in and sit by your fire for a few minutes while you tell me what's happening.'

In the little kitchen with its large black hearth, Meli heard of the 'goings on' at Merlin. Robin listened attentively, waiting to hear news of his hero. As Mrs. O'Toole, shaking with emotion, came to the end of her story and told of Con's arrest, Robin, sitting on the wooden stool in the chimney corner, gritted his teeth with rage. Who could take his Con away? He'd kill anyone who did.

Stunned by the news of what had befallen her home, Meli drove down the long avenue lined with stalwart beeches. Somewhere in the back of her mind she heard her parents' words: 'To an Irishman? My dear girl, you cannot be serious.'

Where indeed and to what climax had her marriage brought her now? Time would tell, but not yet.

The lights of the car lured Mrs. Murphy to her kitchen door. She looked sombre, but Robbie's kisses and hugs soon thawed her generous heart. Over a cup of unwanted tea, Meli heard her cook recount the events of the last two days. She still had to face her husband.

Danger unites

At ten o'clock, Alec returned from his travels. He greeted his wife coolly. 'You've been getting around lately.'

She sat silent on the sofa; Robin had almost forcibly been sent to bed. This meeting was not an ordeal for a child of ten years old to attend.

How was London? The question was received with silence. Outside birds gave their night calls. Distantly, Meli heard the curlew's sad call. Her heart overflowed. Across the dimly lit room sat the man for whom she had incurred her family's permanent displeasure. Now they had drifted so far apart and were both aware of it; danger stood at the door of their lives. Part of that danger she had created, the greater part. The rest was the fault of this odd land which still searched for a remote peace. Nervously she told of her migraine and Dr. Lyster's advice of immediate treatment. The story sounded hollow and Alec did not help by remaining silent. Then she told of Robin's school epidemic, but her husband only stared into the peat fire.

After a long silence he spoke. 'I took some photographs in London, which will interest you. They are in the developing tray now. Let's go and look at them.'

Meli's heart almost stopped beating – the photographic room, Martin's sick room. In a flash she remembered the camp bed. Her only one hope was that Con had remembered to return it to the workshop, or hide it somewhere, after their departure. Not only had the house been searched in her absence, but her husband had chosen to use of all places in that rambling old house that one small but dangerously vital room.

'Aren't you interested?' Alec's voice brought her back.

'Yes, yes of course. I'd love to see them.'

As they descended the stairs in silence, Meli felt like a puppy being led to the scene of its crime, there to receive punishment. Alec walked before her carrying a lamp. The door stood open and, with indescribable relief, she watched her husband walk straight into the room. No bed barred his way. God, bless Con: she would never think him forgetful again, even when she found the glasshouses unwatered from time to time. Alec held his plates in turn before the light and Meli, relieved from fear, showed enthusiastic interest in each scene.

At ease for the first time in several days, Meli took her husband's arm as they walked up the stairs. The house was quiet. In the smoking room, Alec poured himself a drink and walked to his writing desk. From a drawer, he took his own stained white pyjama jacket. 'Who used this?' The words, though softly spoken, sounded like marbles dropped on a china dish.

'Why should I know? What an extraordinary place to hide your dirty clothes. Put it in the basket in your dressing room and Phoebe will empty it tomorrow.'

'Normally I don't need to hide my clothes, but it seems that somebody else forgot to do so on this occasion.'

'Alec, what are you talking about?' Meli was fighting to appear unmoved by this ghastly revelation. Of course she recognised the pyjama jacket which Martin had worn. There were the iodine stains on the shoulder.

Her husband was watching her closely and the tone of her voice irritated him. Raising his own, he almost shouted: 'Don't be a bloody fool. Can't you see the mess we're both in?'

Once more Meli tried: 'There's no need to insult me and at the same time wake Robin.'

167

In his rage and frustration, Alec had forgotten that the boy was sleeping in a small spare room across the corridor from the smoking room. 'Don't you know where I found this?'

'No, why should I?'

'I – not the Military – found it in my photographic room,' he hissed the words.

'What has that to do with me?'

Neither of them heard Robin's door open. Nothing about his wife, her vagaries, her long hours closeted in her library when he would have liked her company, nothing aggravated him as much as this long-nosed superior attitude, the 'better than thou' tone in her voice. He stared at her, his face flushed in anger, for he knew she was using this weapon to shield her guilt.

'Then how do you account for my finding this beside it? I'm not aware of us using that particular room as our bedroom. Merlin offers better facilities.' His voice was also bitter now. From Alec's hand fluttered one of Meli's own lace-edged handkerchiefs. She made her last stand.

'Alec, I think you must have become affected by something on you trip. Are you ill? What is all this rubbish about the photographic room being our bedroom?'

He handed her the handkerchief and threw some peat sod into the dying fire.

'However long it takes, you and I have got to have this out and get matters between us straightened out. We are in danger, Meli! You challenge me about my state of mental health and rubbish about a bedroom.' Alec paused and then slowly, step by step, answered her challenge. 'I found my camp bed set up in my photographic dark room. It is never used by anybody but myself. All day I have been trying discreetly to find out how it got there. Ed, whom I trust, believes that it is still in his workshop with my other kit. The girls admitted that they have not been to clean the room for two months. Mrs. Murphy assures me that she has never put foot in the dark 'pokey hole' in her life, feeling certain it's full of spiders. Who is left? Then I find my stained pyjama jacket and your personal handkerchief. Meli you have been shielding someone in that room and that someone you drove to Dublin in the Ford yesterday. Don't deny it, because I saw you on the road.'

Meli sank down into a chair. What was the use of hiding the truth from her husband any longer? By the Grace of God, it was he that had found the damning items of proof, not the Military. Alec was right: they and their home were in great danger. How much more she knew this than her husband, who stood before her justly perplexed and angry.

'Alec, either I must tell you all or remain silent. My story, which will shock you deeply, will not stand compromise.'

'For God's sake, tell me everything and quickly. We may not have much time to plan our defences and, if what I suspect is true, reprisals are swift and costly. Even our lives may be involved.'

With her voice shaking with strain and emotion from these last exhausting days, Meli told her story, sparing no detail, save her own personal feelings towards Martin McCarthy. At the mention of his name, Alec felt a cold shiver run down his back. The article in the newspaper he had read at breakfast in the Shelbourne left no doubt of the Black and Tans' fury at the murder of one of their leaders. Their search of Merlin showed that the scent had led them there. They had taken Con away for questioning. Now from his wife he knew the reason why. God alone knew what that frail youth would say under Black and Tan 'pressure'. At the end of Meli's almost incredible story, they sat in silence until Alec spoke almost as if to himself:

'How on earth did Con become involved in this mess?'

There was a slight noise, the clearing of a throat. In the doorway, clad in his red dressing gown stood Robin. Before Alec could reprove him, the boy said softly, 'Dad, I heard you shouting as you came up the stairs. You woke me up and afterwards I couldn't get back to sleep. I wanted to come and be with you both but, as I reached the door, Mummy had started to tell her story; and I well, I, er, just couldn't interrupt.'

'So, now you too know all there is to know.'

'Yes Dad. But I know more. You asked how Con got muddled up in all this. I can tell you because I know.'

'You know, Robbie? How could you know, you have been away at school?' It was his mother, shaken at her son having also heard her revelation, her confession of criminal law-breaking.

'Let him speak. Come here boy and tell us what you know.'

The fire burned brightly now, revived by the peat which Alec had thrown on it, and Robbie, his hair tousled from sleep, walked barefoot across the room and sat on the low fire stool near his father. It seemed to Alec Casemond that the boy wished to associate his story and any guilt that it might contain with that of his mother's.

'Robbie, as I have told your mother, we have put ourselves in serious danger. You must try hard to tell us your story from the beginning and completely. Do not leave any details out; it may help us should we be questioned.'

In contrast to his mother's embarrassment, the nine-year-old boy, now wide awake, appeared to take pleasure in recounting the secrets of the Firgrove cavern. He no longer even felt disloyal to his beloved Con, nor to Kevin, and his father's words convinced him that the telling of his exciting tale could only help the two men. Such is the reasoning of youth and in this instance his choice of action was correct. Though his father had been a respected British Army officer, Robin could not believe that he would hurt Con, and, anyhow, his mother had done much more to help Martin.

Happily and well he told his story, from the moment of finding the wounded youth in the cavern. Only did he omit the taking of his father's water bottle and the Merlin horse blanket. Mrs. Murphy's chicken he told of proudly, for he felt that was a really daring act.

'Did you know this man, Robbie, had you ever seen him before?'

'No; Dad, I hadn't, and, when I asked him his name, he said he hadn't got one. Con called him Kevin.'

'What did Con tell you of the Rynah affair?'

Somewhat crushed, Robin had to confess that Con had 'dried up' on him. 'It's not for the likes of you, Master Robbie,' he had said. The boy copied his hero well enough to make his parents smile.

The fire threw its soft yellow light round the panelled room and on to the faces staring into it. Robin's copying of Con's voice had brought a lightness to the tense atmosphere and had also helped to end their conversation. Now each knew each other's story and there was little more to be said. In the quietness of the room, Alec found it almost impossible to believe the two stories he had just heard – particularly his wife's. It was, after all, only natural for a small boy to be thrilled by finding a sick and mysterious man in his personal hide-out. Whether his leg had been wounded innocently or not would matter little to him, compared with the general excitement of his find, and not to have helped someone who was injured would have been unthinkable. With Meli, the whole situation was different. She, an adult, finding Martin being taken into the potting shed, had actually invited him into Merlin itself. Of course, it was kind and humane, but the danger and risk involved, including the car journey to Dublin, made him wonder why she had done it.

A scent of danger

Captain Bert Johnstone was a short stockily-built man of thirty-three. His record was not an attractive one and the remission of a five year jail sentence for armed hold up with violence was gained through a signed undertaking that he would serve to keep rebellious Irish elements under control.

This in fact meant that he had arrived recently for the first time in his life in Ireland, ill clad, but determined to gain from his experience financially, if not socially. As a child, life in a Liverpool slum had been hard. His father, a drunkard, frequently thrashed him for a trivial offence and, on one occasion, had kicked him through a door. The splintered glass panel, when he had tried to defend himself, left permanently its marks on his cheek and right hand. There was never enough money in the house for his mother to buy food and at last, after a school outing, he had been able to help her. During their high tea of sausages and mashed potato, young Bert, only nine years old, had noticed the teacher's handbag lying on a chair next to the door. As he went to the lavatory, she was at the far end of the café trying to maintain order amongst her student flock. The bag was not closed and near the clip lay a ten shilling note. Within a second it was in his pocket and, from that moment, the lad had learnt that it was easy to take from those who had and give it to those who had not. At least he thought he had learnt the art, until the fateful day, almost three years ago now, when he let himself down a cold Hampstead stack pipe, right into the arms of two waiting policemen. More painful even than the five year sentence he received was the thought of losing that superb pearl necklace – and yes the sapphire ring set in platinum. Sapphires were outstandingly his favourite stones.

Because of his 'little spot of trouble', Bert Johnstone had not seen war service – a pity really, for he might have taken the opportunity of knowing a healthier way of life. Instead, his outlook was narrow and bitter. 'Get what you can while you can' was his theory, and as such this legalised jail break was exactly what he needed. God bless that crummy little Welshman – Lloyd George.

Bert Johnstone was no fool, and his quick witted ways secured rapid promotion. Typically it was he who had suggested to his superior officer, Major MacTaggart, the 'gate crash' on Merlin. But where had it got him? Now, not only was Angus dead, but he himself was left with the 'clear up' and what a mess it all was. Not one of these stinking rotten bastards knew a thing; butter wouldn't melt in their lousy drooping mouths. It was he too who had found himself dancing with the Merlin hostess, Mrs. Casemond, herself an Englishwoman and a damned snob. Never had he been more relieved than when the band had stopped playing, so that he could escape from that cold arrogant woman. And her husband! He, Bert Johnstone, had watched that character's reaction to his little idea 'of a bit of sport' on New Year's Eve: the cold self control at their unheralded and unwelcome arrival, the curled lip evident at their departure. Well, at least they had wrecked that smug but appetising buffet – a laugh on all those toffee-nosed guests when they went simpering later to 'have a little refreshment'.

He tapped his pencil on the plain wooden table which served as a desk. Upon it were piles of paper; and every one of them concerned the murder of his superior officer. Since that fateful moment in the early hours of New Year's Day, Bert Johnstone had done nothing – absolutely nothing – but search,

search, search for Angus MacTaggart's murderers. Now it was possible that a certain Martin McCarthy, an employee of Colonel Kernahan – the only sane chap he had met in this godforsaken backwoods – was his quarry. Whether it was or was not actually this Martin McCarthy mattered little to him: at least it would serve as a lesson if he was shot out of hand; and it would also impress an increasingly worried Dublin Castle. What worried him much more was that every trail he had acquired through his contacts led to a dead end.

In these last days, he had become convinced that a forceful I.R.A. cell existed in the Rynah district and that Martin McCarthy was its guiding force. When the Police Barracks were burned, Colonel Kernahan claimed a victim, who had obligingly screamed in answer to the Colonel's bullet. When his friend Angus had been cruelly murdered, there had again been a victim. A reprisal. Where was he? Where were they? Why did his mind and thoughts turn towards Merlin – the home of Captain Alexander Casemond, an Irish gentleman, and his cold English wife? Where did they fit into this complex picture? At least he now had the possibility of finding answers to some of these questions. Con O'Toole was 'waiting below' to be interrogated. This Con had worked for the Casemond family since boyhood: he was delicate, anyone could observe that, and therefore could very likely be bullied into filling in many of the blanks that were frustrating Bert Johnstone.

'Where's your leader – you know who I mean – that murdering sod, Martin McCarthy?'

Con stood before the desk. He was unshaven and the high colour which lit his cheekbone was reflected in the dark, dark eyes: 'Mister, what ever your name is, why didn't you stay home in your blasted country?' He knew what he was saying and he knew what the price to be paid for such a remark.

The Black and Tan clenched his fists in fury. Slowly, he arose and walked towards Con. His face contorted with rage, he stood before the thin Irish youth. 'How dare you?' he hissed and brought the palm of his right hand across the other's face. To his added fury, Con only smiled – a sweet gentle smile, tinged with patronage.

'Who shields you lot of crawling traitors? Your precious Captain Casemond, I presume?'

The face of the youth, until this moment infuriatingly calm, flushed slightly.

'Go on, tell me and I'll make it worth your while.' Johnstone's voice became almost wheedling. Back in England, members of each class stood united. Surely this stupid lad could tell that he was in similar company to his own. On the other hand, Captain Casemond was from a very different drawer and was Con's employer. By Bert Johnstone's reckoning, he should be hated or at least envied by his employees.

'Look here man!'

To his surprise, the youth drew himself up until he towered above the desk. His mouth twisted into a look of scorn as he gave his answer: 'Wouldn't any man, any human being, be doing the right thing to protect his own from the likes of you?'

As Con heard the words coming from his lips, he knew too late that he had in his cold fury and disgust played into the hands of this despicable foreigner, who held him in his power. As proof of his error, he watched a smile, not a pleasant one, cross his interrogator's face. Captain Johnstone had reason to smile: the first part of his plan had worked, not perhaps entirely efficiently, in that he had not been able to get this stubborn youth to betray his master outright. This he, Bert, would have done for a fiver in similar circumstances. Nevertheless, the old trick had worked. Con O'Toole had jumped to the defence of his employer, which really could be twisted, when he prepared his next report to Dublin Castle, into implicating the owner of Merlin as a sympathiser with the Sinn Féin movement.

The second part of his plan was infinitely more subtle and he hoped equalling rewarding. On the previous day, two of his men, searching in the neighbourhood of Merlin for clues that might lead to the whereabouts of Martin McCarthy, had called on a certain doctor, always a possible source of information, by the name of Lyster. The old man had shown complete surprise at the name, which in turn made his inquisitors suspicious. As they started their car at the doctor's gate, they noticed a well worn path leading into, what proved to be on the ordnance survey map, the Firgrove Wood, part of the Merlin estate. They stopped their engine and decided to see where the path led. In so doing, they had found the cavern, which in turn had provided three priceless clues. By sifting patiently through a pile of charred papers, they had found what could possibly have been a list of dates – for what? – a meeting perhaps? If by luck they were right, then Martin McCarthy, now accepted by the Authorities as the local I.R.A. leader, might attend. Back at Captain Johnstone's H.Q. the charred paper studied under a strong light had shown one date which could read as January 16th – in other words, today's date. For this reason also, he had been determined to get the youth in for interrogation to try and detect whether he was nervously impatient. On the contrary, results had been disappointing; for Con had appeared in full control, except when his employer's character was questioned. Well he, Bert Johnstone, had not been successful in his many burglaries without himself possessing a certain shrewdness which the army had not given him.

'You are under arrest, and if Martin McCarthy is not found within three days, you will be shot for having helped in his escape.'

Con knew well that the Black and Tans, unlike the Royal Irish Constabulary, did not wait for the decisions of the court. They took their own. The threat of being shot meant less to him at this moment than that his freedom was now at an end. Tonight a meeting should take place at the cavern and Martin's last plea to Con, as the Mistress had set off for Dublin, was that he should at all cost see that it was cancelled, at least until the heat of the search for Martin had died down. With so little time in hand after Martin's departure, he had managed to contact all save one of the members, Joe Connery. Now it was too late, he could have kicked himself.

Five minutes after Con had been led away, the soldier who locked the door was back with Captain Johnstone. The latter smiled and lit a cigarette:

'We are making progress, Roberts. The idiot would not commit his master, but his defence of him can be suitably distorted in a report to the Castle. In view of that charred timetable, I'd lay a good bit that, if this chap is part of the Rynah cell, he would dearly like to be free this evening. If I'm right, he could lead us to the real 'kill', including Martin McCarthy.'

Mike Roberts himself had no prison record. He was one of the large army of failures who could not get settled after the War. His gratuity had dwindled until the suggestion of joining the Black and Tans and 'giving the Irish hell' sounded quite a pleasant solution to his personal problems. It was he who had discovered the secret meeting place in Firgrove Wood and he was mighty proud of himself, having noticed that track opposite the doctor's gate. It had seemed odd to him that such a well-used path should lead nowhere, and since they had spent days openly searching the countryside, why not be sure that nowhere meant nowhere?

Johnstone looked at his watch: it was already two o'clock

on this winter's day. 'Did you put him on the ground floor as I suggested?' Roberts nodded. 'Take him some food then – bully beef and bread will do – and as you come out close the door and carelessly let it slip back on its catch. Better still, drink a couple of stiff whiskies first and act as if you were sloshed. Be sure and tell any of the men you see, to go to the canteen and leave the front entrance free.'

Roberts departed with alacrity, anxious to avail himself of two free whiskies; and Johnstone sat back in his chair smiling as he endeavoured to draw four-leaved shamrocks on the blotting pad. So much depended on that charred piece of paper and its few blurred dates. If he was correct, even though it was a long shot, this was going to be a night to remember.

Merlin was in fact only eight miles distant, but the Black and Tans knew that time must be allowed for Con to lead them hopefully to their quarry. Every detail had been thought out even to the bicycle which was propped near the front gate. Two men had left already, well armed, to take up positions in Firgrove Wood. If necessary, and there was a likelihood of their being overwhelmed, they were to act only as observers; but, at all costs, they must follow Martin McCarthy's movements, should he show himself at the cavern. Johnstone himself had a large Crossley truck ready at the rear of the house, loaded with guns and ammunition. In addition, he had ordered that several extra cans of petrol be placed in the truck. Who knew where this chase, if chase it was to be, would lead them, and in 1921 petrol stations were rare objects on the country roads of Ireland.

Shortly, he heard thunderous footsteps stumbling up the wooden staircase, accompanied by a handful of choice oaths. The door was flung open and Roberts lurched into the room. Either he was putting on a very excellent act or he had exceeded the permitted ration of whiskey, for his display was quite convincing.

'I've fed the bastard, not that he deserves it, and locked him up securely. Now I'm off for a kip and I suggest 'Mon Capitaine' that you do the same.' The words rang out down the staircase, loud and clear, and they were concluded with a hearty belch. Roberts winked as he left the room, again not quite closing the door.

Johnstone took his chair to the window, placing it an angle where he could be shielded by a casually drawn curtain. He could feel his nerves tensing with excitement and suspense. About to take place was the first event in his carefully spun web. The house had gone very quiet; only a distant mutter of voices came from the canteen – otherwise silence.

Would that dumb youth even notice the prison door? Would he dare to take advantage of it even so? His thoughts were answered by the slight creak of a hinge somewhere in the house. Johnstone stopped breathing and came as near to prayer as he had ever done in his life. Any move now would wreck his plan – pray heaven that none of his men would use the main hall. The noise must have come from Con's door, or it would have been accompanied by heavy footsteps. Moments that seemed like hours passed, and Johnstone could only sit silently and helplessly watching from his window. There was the bicycle just visible, discreetly protruding from an evergreen bush near the gate. Would the bait be taken? The palm of his hands had become wet with apprehension.

Quickly, and almost before he could believe what he was waiting for, a figure had glided on to the bicycle saddle and was already receding down the drive. The chase was on, but patience was required in order to allow the youth to get clear from his erstwhile prison.

A glorious day

Alec Casemond knew his wife and realised the futility of trying
to continue the conversation. They had both taken a very
sleepy Robin back to his bed and the warmth of his presence –
so missed since he had started going to school – seemed to
draw them closer together. Here they were, all three back safe
and sound in Merlin – and tomorrow was another day. As Alec
kissed his wife goodnight, some tremors of their early married
life filtered through his veins. For him, at least, it was a very
happy night.

Next morning, the sun shone bright and clear, and it was
already nine o'clock when Robin followed by Scram burst into
the bedroom. 'Lord, you are a sleepy old pair! I've been up for
hours.' Jumping on to the bed, he poured out the story of his
morning, his words falling over each other with excitement. As
suddenly as he arrived, so he darted away again, leaving Alec
and Meli, gasping and still rubbing the sleep from their eyes.
His effervescent cheer had infected Alec. Why worry about the
past? It was a glorious day and he longed for a game of golf.

'Come on Meli, come with me. You needn't play; just
walk round as you used to do. There are always people at the
Club House wanting a game.'

Meli hesitated and Alec feared that the coldness, so
apparent of late, would kill his happy if selfish idea. 'But, what
about Robin?'

'What about him? It's his first day back and you know
how many things he always has to see and do after he has been
away from Merlin for five minutes. I know, we'll take

sandwiches and send him over to Eila House to report to his Grandmother. She'd love his company.' It happened, as with so many grandmothers, that Emma Casemond came easily under the spell of her small grandson.

After breakfast – Robin had eaten long before – Alec Casemond talked seriously to his son about the previous night's conversation. The boy seemed quite aware of its seriousness.

'Well, Dad, I would never have told anybody my story if I hadn't thought it would help; and as for Mum, I think she did a wonderful brave thing.'

'My dear boy, what you think is not the point. Don't you realise that it is a criminal offence to shelter, or even help anyone who is wanted by the Police?'

'Those creatures aren't Police – you should hear what the boys at school say about them. Why, they even say that in Dublin ...'

'Robin,' his father spoke firmly, 'you are a child and an excitable one. What you heard last night – and I wish you hadn't – you must forget. Now! This minute! I want you to promise me that, if you love your mother, which you do, you must never, never speak of it.'

Robin was on the verge of tears. Last night he had been a 'grown up' on an equal footing with his parents, sharing their individual secrets and discussing them openly and frankly. Now he was ordered to forget them as if they had never happened. With difficulty he forced a smile. 'Alright Dad. I'll do what you say, but on one condition.' His father looked at him sharply, but before he could speak, the boy continued brightly, 'and that is that you never call me a child again. I am a schoolboy now, remember?'

God, how different Merlin was when this lad was around. If only there was a decent day school anywhere near, he'd never let him return to Dublin. And so it was that as his parents drove off happily to the Golf Club, Robin wandered across the fields to Eila House.

Alec won his match against his old friend, Henry Lister, and it had been agreed that whoever lost would be the host at dinner. Although both Casemonds wanted to get back to Merlin, and Robin and certainly did not need a late night after the rigours of the day before, it seemed unkind to Henry not to honour their bargain. Robin, Alec told himself, would be alright; he had Mrs. Murphy and the two maids. The day had been a glorious one, almost like early spring, and he had easily been able to shake off the sombre memories of the previous day. Meli had not been with him to the golf course for many a day and Henry Lister kept a good table and the best wines in the district. Even Meli herself seemed contented. She had admired his golf and chatted with the two caddies. Ireland was a great country to forget things and, after years of war and danger, Alec Casemond, as he drove the Vauxhall behind Henry's car, thought of their recent experiences as all part of 'the troubles' – that phrase so cryptically chosen to cover the Irish Revolution.

The trap closes

Con had ridden a bicycle all his life but never had he pedalled as furiously as now. No one stopped him on his way down the long drive and, in his relief and haste, he never considered whether his easy escape might have been planned. Now he too was on the run – a criminal fleeing from justice and a wanted man. His only thought was to get Martin's message to Joe Connery and, as he rode blindly along the empty road, he tried to recognise his whereabouts. Round a sharp bend, he came upon a woman driving a donkey cart. He pulled up, jumped off the bicycle and fought for breath to speak to her.

'Holy Saints man, what ails yer? Is it the banshee that's at yer heels?'

Panting, Con asked the way to Rynah, saying he had to get there quick or he'd be in 'a fine old trouble'. The woman laughed as she gave him his directions. Con's breath was coming easier now. He smiled and thanked her, and was off once more – 'with the banshee at his heels'. To go into Rynah he knew was dangerous, but fortunately Joe Connery was staying in a cottage some distance out on a small by-road. Again luck favoured him, for no Military vehicle barred his way.

The message delivered, Con realised that from now on he was a fugitive – homeless and jobless. Badly drawn likenesses with dramatic captions were to be found glued to the corners of public buildings. Con found himself composing his own 'Wanted' notice. 'Wanted – Murderer aged approximately 24, lean, high coloured.' Suddenly with a cold damp hand clutching his heart, he realised that the Gate Lodge was no longer his meagre haven. Even to visit there would place his mother and brother in danger.

The bicycle pedals slowed as he thought aloud. Until now a man 'on the run' was a type of hero. All Ireland – his Ireland – thrilled to the phrase; but now? What should he do? Where should he go? How young, how insignificant he felt. It was cold and a watery sun was quickly setting over those damp marshlands where the curlew lived. The curlew! He knew his destination: a sanctuary, safer than Dublin Castle – Merlin's potting shed. For years he had worked in that rickety old wooden structure, where mice made their nests in spring and in winter moved in for their hibernation. In May, the swallows, just returned from Africa, spring-cleaned their last year's nests and soiled his clean flower pots with their droppings. There he would be at home with his tools, and the soft smell of beech mould would calm and soothe his troubled mind.

It was not until two hours after Con O'Toole's flight that Captain Johnstone summoned his driver and ten of his best men. Calmly, he told them of his plan, and proudly explained the success with which he and Mike Roberts had let the hare slip out of the trap. Now, if his luck held, that same hare would walk into a far bigger trap, taking with him those men who were needed to clear up the whole Rynah affair.

It was not yet dark, for the day had been exceptionally fine and twilight lasted longer than in England. The Crossley drove along the empty road without lights and stopped in a small boreen some distance from Firgrove. Quietly, the men dismounted and, as instructed, they spread in a semi-circle and slid away into the darkening wood. The plan was that they should converge silently on the cavern, which had been described to them on a carefully drawn map. At the sound of the Captain's whistle, they would cock rifles and shoot down any figure seen trying to escape.

So far, so good; but when after half an hour's slow crawl through the trees and undergrowth the Captain, who had taken the central position, arrived near enough to the cavern entrance, he saw nothing and heard no sound. Patiently he waited. Ten minutes passed, half an hour, a full hour. The moon came out and crept up through the tall trees. It was cold now and his optimism began to wane. In its place came a dull rage, for Johnstone realized that his waiting men would be thinking him a fool. He had let O'Toole go and for nothing. How much cosier to have coaxed him to talk – there were so many ways. Perhaps the secret meeting was in his own imagination; or perhaps it was taking place somewhere else, even nearer Merlin than this cold dark wood.

He himself had never entered the cavern and he would damned well take a look at it. Pulling the cork from his hip flask, he took another long slug of whiskey. It tingled through his body and he felt warmer and more confident. In a clear voice, he called out: 'I'm going in to have a look round.' That would let those of his men nearest to him know his intention. Firmly, he strode forward and, at the cavern's entrance, flashed on his electric torch. Inside there was nothing of interest; his men had seen to that on their earlier visit. Only a bundle of scattered straw lay in one corner. What a dank hole it was. He took his flask from his hip pocket, pulled the cork with the hand that held his torch and put the flask to his lips. As he did so, a hand grasped his shoulder and made him jump; the cork fell from his hand into the heap of straw.

'You bloody fool! What the Hell do you think you're doing? Now I've dropped the cork of my flask.' Johnstone flashed his torch on Mike Roberts' grinning face.

'Sorry, Sir. It's so damned cold outside, thought I'd follow you in. Sorry too about the cork. Here I'll find it for you.' Roberts bent down and scattered the straw to the left and right, but with no success.

'Leave it to me, you fool!' Johnstone approached the task with more care. He felt gently with his fingers through the straw. After all, in his former 'profession', it had paid to have a gentle touch.

'Here, what's this?' The Captain's hands fastened on something buried deep in the pile. Roberts shone the torch on an army water bottle. Both men recognised it as such immediately. On it was marked a serial number. Some of the Captain's former enthusiasm returned. He turned the bottle over.

'Hold that light close.' Clearly legible was one word written in ink 'Casemond'. Johnstone's heart gave a leap; here was something tangible and it again smacked of Merlin. What a useful piece of evidence! Quickly he took the rest of the pile apart. At the very bottom lay a brown crumpled blanket. As the two men unfolded it, the torches' light fell on the embroidered initials 'A.C.'. Bert Johnstone smiled as he spoke.

'And against these bits of evidence, Captain Alexander Casemond is going to have a lot of explaining to do.'

In his triumph, the thought of Con O'Toole's possible meeting, even the possibility of catching Martin McCarthy, faded in his delight at challenging Captain Casemond, that arch hypocrite and two-faced traitor, who posed as a gentleman and a loyal subject of King George. The man, who had worn an officer's uniform, was now certainly befriending, shielding and probably was himself, a member of this bloody band of murderers. Johnstone walked to the entrance and shouted.

'Men, I've found something useful! We are off to Merlin where I want to ask a few questions. You may light up. Back to the lorry.'

Around the cavern, torches flashed as men's voices rang out through the sleeping wood.

Robin had always loved his grandmother. She was so strong and yet so gentle with him. Of course, she spoiled him. On this occasion, they had a toffee-making session. This meant heating a pan full of sugar and chocolate powder over the peat fire until it all became a thick mass of almost unstirrable substance. This was turned into a cake tin and left on a draughty window sill to harden. Then after Robin and his grandmother had discussed their problems, as equals, a meat chopper was used to divide the rocklike mass into squares, many of which were consumed before the remaining few were put into a bag to be taken back to Merlin.

Tenderly Emma Casemond kissed the boy's head. He brought so many memories of her own sons, one of whom was Robin's father. They were of a bygone age, when Eila House rang day and night to the shouts of her flock, now scattered, drowned, married or buried in far-off lands. What a curse age was. To be lonely at the end of her life was a cruel blow and one she had never expected.

In the twilight, she watched the proud little figure fading away from her across the large open field. What had life in store for him, long after she was gone, or even round the next moonrise?

Robin walked happily on, swinging the paper bag of toffee. Surely his mother and father would be back from their stupid game of golf and they might allow him to stay up and dine with them.

By the time he reached the end of the big field, a watery moon rose above the dark bank of trees. There in front of him lay the small wooden bridge leading to the water-garden, potting shed and on to the big house.

Robbie wished he had taken the other path by the river. To come near the potting shed made his heart ache. Where was his dear Con? What were they doing to him? Suddenly he felt terribly alone. Even his mother and father had gone off for the day without him. He almost wished he had never left school, although it had seemed so thrilling when his mother drove him away.

The path, the same that his mother had used scarcely a week earlier, passed by the shed. Robbie stopped in front of it.

'If only Con could be there now.' All was silent. Well, he would just have a peep inside for old times' sake. He pushed open the door and sniffed. Yes, there was the same peat smell. He walked inside and stood quite still. The fear of being alone never entered his head. Merlin was his home and this old shed was where he had spent his happiest hours.

The arms which enveloped him in the darkness harboured no ill. Gently, but firmly, they lifted him from the ground.

'Robbie, me darlin', me wild one, what brings you here this dark night?' Con's voice, though hoarse, sounded gentle and soothing in the frightened boy's ear. He threw his arms round Con's neck and hugged him.

'Oh Con, dear Con, I thought I'd never see you again. What have they done to you? Why are you here? Have they let you go free? Oh, you are cold.'

Con carried the boy to a wooden stool and sitting on it himself he held Robbie on his knee and started to tell his story. There was no point in hiding things from him any more.

Ten minutes later, Robin, thrilled at playing his role of provider once more, was off to the big house in search of food and blankets, not for a stranger, but this time for his beloved Con.

Revenge

Without the need for silence, it did not take long for Captain Johnstone and his men to reach their lorry. The chase was on, after days of pent-up nerves and impatience. Johnstone emptied his flask and threw it into the ditch.

'Climb aboard boys, we are going to have a little fun.' The driver already knew his destination. With a roar, the engine started and bright lights pierced the narrow roadway as the lorry shot forward.

At Merlin, the gateway was chained and locked against all comers, but a raucous klaxon horn accompanied by the thump of an engine brought Ed scurrying out of his Gate Lodge.

'Open, or we'll shoot our way through,' called the Captain.

'But the Master's not home,' pleaded Ed. 'I'm expecting him any minute.'

'Oh! So your master's not home,' the voice from the darkness was full of sneer, 'then we'll go ahead and wait for him. Open up, you cringing cur, or we'll shoot you through the padlock.'

As Ed stood helpless in the piercing lights, his mother leapt from the darkness and pulled his arm.

'Ed, for God's sake do what they ask. Yer all I have left, now they've taken Con.' She sobbed out the words.

By now the exhaust fumes had formed a choking fog round the lorry. 'Hurry man, you have five seconds.' Helplessly, Ed pulled the key from his pocket, undid the chain and pushed open first one and then the second heavy iron gate.

As the lorry pulled up on the gravel sweep, Robin was in the act of climbing through the larder window. Quickly, he slid back to the ground and crawled into the nearby laurel bushes.

Once more Captain Bert Johnstone strode Merlin's marble steps. On the former occasion, he had followed his commanding officer, who now lay in his cold grave, foully murdered. This time, he led the way unhindered by MacTaggart's plea for good manners and self-restraint: that they were visitors and it was New Year's Eve and all that guff. Well, all that was in the past; now he would call the tune. In the doorway stood a formidable, red-faced woman, her arms on her hips; behind in the hallway hovered two young ladies, wearing dark blue frocks and white aprons.

'And where do you think you may be going, pray?'

'Pray yourself, you old bag,' Johnstone called back. As the woman ran forward to prevent him from entering the house, he put his foot out, one of the many tricks he had perfected to avoid arrest. The heavy frame toppled ignominiously over a chair and ended up in a crumpled heap of screaming oaths and petticoats. The hoots of male laughter coming up the steps broke poor Mrs. Murphy's spirit. She had tried to defend Merlin alone and now, shamed and ridiculed, she sobbed in her disgrace.

'Back to the kitchen all of you, if you know what is good for you that is,' Johnstone's voice had an ugly harshness. He was no coward, for he had done his burglaries single-handed and that was lonely work. Now dealing with three women and backed by ten tough men, the blood ran to his head.

'To the buffet boys,' he called, as Mrs. Murphy picked herself up and spat in his direction.

'Heathens,' she spluttered.

'Harridan,' he replied, giving her a good slap on the bottom. 'Off to your kitchen before I have to hurry you there with this.' He took from his belt a revolver and twirled it on a finger.

The dining room, which he and his men knew, was lit by two shaded lamps. In the centre was a large highly polished table with two places laid. At the end of the room on a long sideboard stood a silver tray on which were two bottles of whiskey and several glasses.

'Help yourselves lads,' said Bert Johnstone. 'Roberts and I have a little work to do.' Quickly the two men poured and swallowed their slugs of whiskey, then left the room. Outside in the corridor all was quiet.

'Roberts, I'm determined to find evidence. To me this place stinks. If we could find something, anything. Already we have Casemond's water bottle and blanket. I know they could have been stolen, but that's not the way the story is going up to the Castle. Just one more piece of evidence here in this God-damned house and we'll have him.'

It was hard work searching a rambling old house by lamplight, but again Johnstone's former profession stood by him. From room to room he went, not knowing what he sought, but just hoping for something, anything incriminating, for now he was obsessed by the conviction that what he needed lay within these walls. Roberts followed miserably, longing to be back in the dining room, whence the sound of voices grew louder. Obviously, the whiskey would be finished before this fruitless search was over.

At the open door of Alec Casemond's smoking room, they paused. A peat fire burned and the room looked welcoming. Near the window stood Alec's liquor cupboard. H'm, they would pause for a rest, Johnstone decided. The cupboard revealed an abundance of whiskey, just what was needed. The two men lost no time in making up for what they had missed in the dining room. If they were not to find what they sought, at least they could drown their disappointment in Casemond's liquor. The Irish might be hell, but their whiskey was excellent. Soft and mellow, it slid down one's throat. This brand of Casemond's was particularly good. As Bert Johnstone poured out the third round, he raised the bottle to the lamp – fifteen years old, by gad, well who'd have known it? His men were singing now; he could hear them plainly from the dining room. Well, they were following instructions. He had told them to drink what they wanted, but to stay where they were until he and Roberts returned.

Mike's glass was empty. God, how the chap drank!

'Ruddy sink you are old boy. Got any cigarettes?'

'No, blast it! Smoked the f....n' lot.'

'Oh well, not to worry. If this sod's got all this liquor, chances are he'll have gaspers too. OK, leave it to me. I'm good at finding things.'

'Oh yea? Ha ha! You serious, after our grand tour of this 'ere Windsor Castle?'

'Don't be funny boy, we haven't finished yet.'

Casemond's writing table looked a likely place for smokes, for it contained plenty of drawers. Bert slumped down on the comfortable chair before it and pulled a drawer open. A neat pile of stationery, envelopes and postcards was all it contained. He tried the next: scissors, pens, tape, and sealing wax. Blast it! Where were the bloody cigarettes? This liquor was stronger than it looked, deeper than it appeared – like Casemond. Bert's head began to ache. He looked across at Roberts, lounging in a deep armchair. The chair and Roberts moved a little to the right and then back. Slowly Bert leaned forward and pulled at the third drawer. It was locked. Something snapped in his brain. This drawer held what he needed. He pushed away the chair and wrenched at the handle.

The drawer would not move. Standing up, he kicked at it violently.

'Here, hold hard man,' Roberts, who had almost dozed off in his comfortable armchair, rose shakily to his feet. 'What's up?'

Bert's face in the soft lamplight was flushed. He spoke slowly as a man in drink will do, when he wishes to sound impressive. 'Get me somethin' to open this bloody drawer. I don't care what in hell it is, but find it.'

Roberts shuffled round the softly lit room, while Bert continued to pull the drawer frenziedly, until the brass handle came away from its sockets.

'Come on man hurry or that bastard Casemond will be back.'

But Roberts found nothing to hand. Again Bert Johnstone's former profession came to his aid. Through a haze of John Jameson, he remembered another useful trick of his trade.

'Bring me that poker,' he barked out the words as a command. Roberts did as he was instructed. Bert pulled out the second drawer, tipping the contents over the floor. Beneath where it had rested was a thin layer of wood which protected the contents of the bottom drawer from dust. This thin piece of wood was no match for the poker and Johnstone's determination. As it splintered and crumbled, Johnstone peered inside. It was too dark to distinguish the objects the drawer contained. His sensitive fingers would soon tell him what lay within. First, however, there appeared to be something like a cover: it was made of material, probably cotton.

'Bring the lamp nearer, Roberts.' Slowly and carefully Bert extracted through the splintered panel a crumpled pyjama jacket; as he straightened it on the desk top, both men saw the red brown stains on the right shoulder and both men knew they had found something of unusual value. Why indeed should this soiled piece of clothing, if it were innocent, be locked carefully away in a writing desk, instead of being placed in a laundry basket? The drawers on the left side were unlocked and contained nothing of interest, but that locked and now splintered compartment might contain further mysterious objects. Even though the whiskey was swirling on both men's heads, they could still appreciate that there must be good reason for hiding so carefully that blood-stained pyjama jacket. The drawer contained papers of various kinds, cancelled cheques, bundles of receipts. Johnstone's optimism began to wane, as he strewed the papers over the floor. Once more his right hand groped through the splintered wood. The drawer was all but empty now. He pulled out the last remains of Alec Casemond's personal papers. Only one sheet remained, it was handwritten.

As he held it in front of the lamp and read the simple script, Johnstone could hardly believe his eyes. It was a page of instructions with Martin McCarthy at its head and contained a list of names:

> Borra Barracks, burn
> Bridge Kilalin, dynamite
> Extinguish Tan stronghold, leader MacTaggart
> Kevin O'Connor
> Con O'Toole ...

Captain Johnstone did not need to study the other names. Here in his hand lay the document which gave him all he needed. If, after days of searching, he had not found Martin McCarthy in person, at least he had evidence in writing of the rebel's evil work.

As the words fogged before his eyes, he smiled. He could have kissed the sheet of cheap paper which he held.

All the hatred that he nursed against this miserable rebellious land paled to insignificance against the importance of where it had been discovered. Johnstone was no fool, drunk or sober. He knew well that the Irish had long kicked against English domination, which was fair enough for the peasants of whom the population was largely made.

But of the traitor, Casemond, masquerading as a gentleman, loyal to the Crown of England, it was another story.

His instructions had been simple: 'Put down the rebellion, and make Ireland a hell for rebels to live in.' The sheet of paper in his hand required no clearing with Dublin Castle. As McCarthy had acted on its very instructions – burning the Rynah Police Barracks and murdering in cold-blooded ambush Angus MacTaggart – so could he, Albert Johnstone, deal now and summarily with this treacherous wretch, Casemond, who had obviously written the instructions lying in his hand. What further evidence was needed to mete out sufficient punishment? He had been suspicious of Merlin and its inhabitants and now he knew that it was a vital cell of the outlawed I.R.A.

Johnstone was now coldly sober. Any minute Alexander Casemond and his proud English lady would return to their smug mansion. He would organise a suitable welcome for them, if it was the last thing he ever did.

Roberts was dozing on the floor, but his men were still singing down the corridor. Their voices were raucous and he knew that they would be ready to carry out his instructions. They too had no love for this damp, unfriendly land. For a minute he sat fondling the priceless piece of evidence. Then he sprang to his feet. Roberts woke to the kick on his posterior. 'Get up man, we are going into action.'

Roberts belched as he picked himself up off the floor. 'What in Hell's name ... A joke's a joke.'

'Shut up, and do what you're told. Follow me.'

Johnstone's mind was clear as he walked towards the dining room, Roberts shuffling behind. As he pushed the door open, Johnstone was reassured by what he saw. His men were drunk on Casemond's whiskey. They would enjoy the little fun which he was about to give them.

Flames of hate

As time passed, Robin became desperate. Con was cold and hungry. He had boasted that he would return, as he had once before for Kevin, with food and blankets. But from his hideout in the laurel bushes, where in former days he had often hidden from Miss Livingstone, he could still see the silent military lorry. From inside Merlin he heard the voices of the intruders singing their stupid songs.

After what seemed like hours, four men staggered down the front steps, took something from the lorry and returned to the house. He could only wait impatiently until they all decided to leave.

Through the quiet night, he heard one voice above the others. It seemed to be giving instructions, but he could only catch an occasional sentence.

'Soak the carpets. Not there you bloody fool! Here give it to me.' Each remark was followed by laughter.

Robin didn't like it. Where was Mrs. Murphy? She would see them off. Everybody was terrified of her. Why didn't his parents return? If only they would come. Should he go and fetch his Grandmother? She would deal with them! Through the bushes, he watched the Merlin windows. Lamps passed from one to another. Men were busy – doing what? Robbie felt suddenly cold and unhappy. If only he could get some food from the larder and get back to Con. There he would feel safe.

Suddenly he heard a woman scream. It sounded like Mrs. Murphy. What could they be doing to her? Should he go into the house and defend her? He was nine years old and strong. If only his father and mother would return. Hardly able to believe his eyes, he saw Mrs. Murphy, Phoebe and Nellie stagger out of the front door, pushed it seemed by the soldiers. Everyone was shouting and Mrs. Murphy's voice pierced over them all.

'And Heaven punish you and strike you down for your heinous crime.' She was pulling at the uniform of one of the men. Nellie and Phoebe had their arms around each other, as if for protection. Suddenly the arguing voices were silenced by a shout from inside the house.

'Let her go!'

The soldiers started down the steps, pushing Mrs. Murphy before them. Nellie and Phoebe needed no urging; at the sound of the staccato words, they were away into the shadows.

Through the open front door came two soldiers, and as Robin watched, he saw to his horror, through one of the windows in the hall a flickering light. By the second it grew brighter and spread to another and another of the windows. On the gravel sweep stood the soldiers; Mrs Murphy had collapsed on the bottom step. Robin could hear her sobs. Through the front door, wisps of smoke came, and soon they turned into great banks of swirling black cloud. On the air, he could smell a sweet acrid smell. His home, his Merlin, was burning before his eyes.

Con shivered in the potting shed. He was cold and exhausted. Once more his cough started to plague him. He stood up and stretched his arms above him. The shed was dark and lonely. He would stand outside and wait for the lad to return. It had been a long time, but perhaps Robbie had not found it as easy as he boasted to take food from Mrs. Murphy's larder.

As he stood by the shed, he could hear voices, men's voices, coming across the still night air. They came from

Merlin. Maybe the Master had visitors, but why the shouting? He was tired now. If only Master Robbie would return, he could lie down and sleep on the damp shed floor, for tomorrow he must leave and hide himself somewhere. He knew not where, but now, he reminded himself, he too was 'on the run'.

As the shouting continued, Con saw, as in a dream, a light from the big house. At first it flickered, and then took hold. Now, as he watched, it grew into a brighter light, engulfing the hall. Then he heard the grinding of an engine, and the roar of a lorry – the Black and Tans, Con knew, had struck again. Through the winter, they had burned houses where they suspected opposition to their authority. But why Merlin? How could they know that Martin had lain hidden there from their fury? Suddenly his heart went cold. Whatever the reason for their action, he knew that little Robbie had, for his sake alone, gone to the house, now belching flames, to fetch food and blankets. He could not stand here and watch Merlin burn before his eyes, with the boy trapped inside it.

His job was to find Robbie at all cost, and no second could be wasted. As he ran across the garden, flames leapt higher, but no sound of voices reached him, only the crackling of timbers.

The side door, which so recently he used to visit Martin was unlocked, and as yet the flames had not succeeded in reaching that end of the house. His own safety meant nothing to him.

'Robbie, Robbie?' he shouted, above the increasing noise of the fire. No answer came to him. Alright, he could search the house quickly. The larder, pantry and kitchen on the ground floor were empty. No one answered his shouts. Then he must try on the next floor. The stairs from the photograph room were clear of flames, but smoke had started to come down from the smoking room. As he ran up the stairs, two at a time, he knew that danger was near at hand. Hot gusts of smoke came and disappeared. Again he called frantically, 'Robbie, Robbie?' but still his calls went unanswered. The centre of the house was now aflame and the main corridor towards the front hall was impassable. If he climbed on above the smoking room, he could reach the bedroom floor. Perhaps the boy had decided to go to his bedroom and wait until morning to try and bring him food. As Con reached the top floor, he realised that Robbie's room lay at the far end of the house. His only hope was to cross along the top corridor. Blindly he pushed forward, smoke filling his lungs. It was dark and he felt that he was choking. Staggering, he groped his way to a window and pulled it open.

Robin had watched the Army lorry depart, and after it he shouted all the words he had learned in the stable yard. The noise made by the fire was increasing, and suddenly wind whipped the flames further, until the whole of the centre of Merlin was an inferno – as yet the East wing and top floor remained dark.

On the wind, he thought he heard his name called; and running from his hideout in the laurels, he called back: 'I'm here, I'm here.' The noise which the fire created drowned his shrill boy's voice. Every second, the nightmare grew bigger. The hall and main rooms were now a huge furnace, beautifully terrible to a young and impressionable mind. Suddenly, he saw a window above the blazing hall open and a figure stand before it. It was Con!

Henry Lister's reputation as a host was never in question. As Alec drove the Vauxhall home with Meli at his side, he felt happier than he had been for a long time. Somehow the crisis through which they had just passed had cleared the air. The barrier which had crept slowly between them had receded. The frankness with which they faced the events of these last days had healed and soothed the spirit of hostility between them, and of which both were aware. He put his hand on hers, and to his joy his wife responded. Hers was warm and gentle – not cold and frigid as he had so often found.

Kahirloch slept as they drove down the long street, and it was not until a mile beyond the village that they noticed that bright light in the sky.

'God Meli! It's Merlin.' The car jumped forward from its leisurely pace, as Alec rounded the remaining turns on two wheels. Merlin's gates stood open and unguarded. The sky was bright and clouds of smoke filled the drive as the Vauxhall sped up to the house. Lit by the flames, Alec and Meli saw a forlorn group of people helplessly watching their proud home burn. As he ran towards them, he heard his son's voice crying out above the roar of the flames.

'Con, come down quickly! Con, it's blazing beneath you!' Then suddenly with a rending crash the hall ceiling collapsed into the roaring flames below. Robbie, helpless, saw the silhouette slide away and disappear, down into that furnace which was devouring his home before his very eyes.

'I saw him, I tell you. I know it was Con. He was there at the window and now ....' His voice trailed away in a sob: 'He's gone for ever – dear, dear Con.'

Epilogue

Standing before the window of a living room in Cheshire, Alexander Casemond brooded over his misfortune. Each member of his family had, in their way, contributed to the disaster that befell Merlin.

His wife had protected and concealed a much wanted man. His son had kept secret the whereabouts of the water bottle and the house blanket, both bearing his name, and he himself had omitted to burn the sheet of paper which he had found in his own photographic room, and had kept secret from his wife. It was that damning document, containing the name of Martin McCarthy and the work he should carry out in furtherance of freedom, which in the end had sentenced them to exile.

He could only pray now that the British Government would realise their rule was over, stop the bloodshed and give his country the freedom they had won. Only then could his family return home.

Postscript

Six months later, on 11 July 1921, truce was declared in Ireland.

Coming soon ... *ATLANTIC AFFAIR*

Imogen at Banagher with 'running sails' set.

Alec, Meli and Robin return to Ireland once independence is declared.

In 1930 Alec makes a voyage in his 26 ft yacht *Imogen*, which was described by the *Tatler* at the time as 'an epic of the sea'. Having invented sails which 'enabled a yacht to run indefinitely before the wind', he set sail single-handed from Ireland following the route around the world taken by his friend Conor O'Brien in the yacht *Saoirse* – old Irish for Freedom.

Robbie has left school and Meli is alone with her books and her garden.

In *Atlantic Affair*, their lives explode in adventure and love.

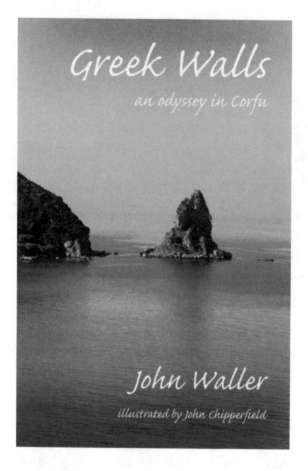

Greek Walls (ISBN 0954788702) starts with John and his Danish wife staying in Peter's one-room stone shepherd's hut in Corfu. With rats in the roof, they leave after one night. With money from a year's work in New York and the help of Peter and his Greek friends, in 1971, they buy land above the sea on the spectacular and deserted west coast and build a modest summer house.

Corfu Sunset (ISBN 0954788710) tells how, in retirement, they defeat their Greek neighbour who has been pumping sewage on their land, construct a road up the mountain, restore their villa and celebrate a great Greek success.

John Waller was educated at Cambridge Unversity, trained as a Systems Engineer at IBM and founded a computer company. He was a Liberal councillor in Richmond for 17 years and three times parliamentary candidate for Twickenham.

In 2004 he published *Greek Walls*, memories of his life in Corfu from 1966. In 2005 he published the sequel, Corfu Sunset, which was described by the *Daily Mail* as 'essential reading for anyone thinking of moving abroad to a place in the sun'.

Peter Waller, John's half-brother, was born in Ireland in 1911. He worked in the American Red Cross in World War II, as house manager at the Royal Opera House, Covent Garden, London, as salesman of vast Crown Derby dinner sets to the sheikhs and kings in the Middle East and as joint founder of the American School in London.

He was a friend of Gerald Durrell, author of *My Family and Other Animals*, and organiser of his US fund-raising tour. In retirement he spent much of the year in Corfu, appearing as a major character in *Greek Walls*. He died in 1990.